AMENITY HORTICULTURE

Roger Bennett

M.A., M.Hort. (RHS), Dip.S.M., Dip.Hort., M.I.Hort., A.B.I.A.C.

KIRKLEY HALL LIBRARY

D0543195

This book is to be returned on or before
the last date stamped below.

1 6 JAN 1997	1 8 MAR 2004
– 3 MAR	2 4 OCT 2007
– 8 1998	
1 1998	NUV 2007
	2 8 NOV 2007
–6. OCT. 2000	1 9 DEC 2007
31. OCT. 2000	0 3 NOV 2014
23. JAN. 2002	
10. APR. 2002	
25. APR. 2002	
10. MAR 2003	

11 II   635.9

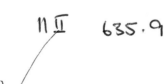

M
MACMILLAN

© Roger Bennett 1991

All rights reserved. No reproduction, copy or transmission
of this publication may be made without written permission.

No paragraph of this publication may be reproduced, copied or
transmitted save with written permission or in accordance with
the provisions of the Copyright, Designs and Patents Act 1988,
or under the terms of any licence permitting limited copying
issued by the Copyright Licensing Agency, 90 Tottenham Court
Road, London W1P 9HE.

Any person who does any unauthorised act in relation to
this publication may be liable to criminal prosecution and
civil claims for damages.

First published 1991 by
THE MACMILLAN PRESS LTD
Houndmills, Basingstoke, Hampshire RG21 2XS
and London
Companies and representatives
throughout the world

ISBN 0–333–53656–8

A catalogue record for this book is available
from the British Library.

Printed in China

10   9   8   7   6   5   4   3
00   99   98   97   96   95   94   93

CONTENTS

ACKNOWLEDGEMENTS

The author and publishers would like to thank

Horticultural Trades Association
The Institute of Horticulture (IOH)
Health and Safety Executive
Pirbic Northern Limited

for permission to reproduce copyright material and

Askham Bryan College of Agriculture and Horticulture, York
Mr M Rylance, Photographer
Wakefield District College
Jan Bennett

for their assistance and support.

NVQ 'AMENITY HORTICULTURE'

Levels 1 and 2 should be in place for the start of the academic year 1992.

Level 1
This is a single qualification made up of the following five units of competence:

Level 2
The Level 2 qualification is made up of the following 'Core' competences:

The 'Core' units are intended to be taken in conjunction with unit options as follows:

Option 1 - Core plus

Option 2 - Core plus

Option 3 - Core plus

Option 4 - Core plus

AMENITY HORTICULTURE

INTRODUCTION: HEALTH AND SAFETY

Since the introduction of the Health and Safety at Work Act (HSWA) in April 1974, Amenity Horticulture like all other industries has had to follow the legal requirements on health and safety as laid down under the Act.

Like other technological industries, Amenity Horticulture is continually making advances in each of its sectors. Mechanisation is widespread within the Amenity sector, for example machines, computers and a wide range of electrically operated equipment are used. Obviously the use of mechanical equipment is potentially hazardous, but the hazards and risks can be greatly reduced if we observe a set of safety rules. Examples of such rules are:

1. Follow manufacturers' instructions.
2. Know the safe system of work.
3. Be trained in the use of the machine or piece of equipment you are using.
4. Wear the necessary protective clothing.
5. Know what to do in an emergency.

Everyone should know about the Health and Safety at Work Act. It is not just a matter for employers. Responsible employees should know what the Act says and appreciate what it sets out to do. One of its important objectives is to bring together both employer and employees to work on Health and Safety. Good health and safety at work requires the co-operation of both parties.

About the 1974 Act

Whether you are an employer, an employee or a self-employed person, including those who work as members of a family business, you have legal duties under the Health and Safety at Work Act.

The Act provides a legal framework to protect the health and safety of all persons who are affected by work activities. This means you must protect not only yourself and anyone you employ, but others such as the general public. Even if you rent or lease a building or provide equipment to users, you still have health and safety responsibilities.

Health and Safety at Work Act – Employers

In carrying out your duties to employees you must ensure that:

1. The workplace is safe.
2. Plant and machinery are safe and meet the set standards.
3. Safe systems of work are set and followed.
4. Noise, dust and fumes are kept within safe levels.
5. Substances and articles are stored, used and transported safely.
6. The necessary protective clothing and equipment are provided.
7. Employees have healthy working conditions, including washing and toilet facilities, adequate heating, light, ventilation, etc.
8. The necessary training, information and supervision is provided.

Employers must also provide, free, any protective clothing and equipment which are required by law. And, if you employ five or more workers, you must prepare a written safety policy and ensure your employees know of its content.

Health and Safety at Work Act – Employees

As an employee you must take reasonable care of your own health and safety and must not take risks or endanger others. You must also co-operate with your employer on health and safety matters.

Health and Safety at Work Act – Self-employed

Since most of the work you are likely to do within the horticultural industry is carried out under similar conditions to those of employed people, it follows that you must also take reasonable precautions to protect yourself and any others who may be affected by your work activities.

Health and Safety at Work Act – Suppliers

Anyone who designs, manufactures, imports or supplies an article for use at work, or erects or installs an article, must make sure that it does not present a health and safety risk when set, used, cleaned or maintained by a person at work.

The same applies to substances with regard to their handling, processing, storage and transportation. Any article or substance supplied for use at work must come with its own up-to-date information on health and safety.

 TO DO

Should you require more infomation about the HSWA, contact your local Agricultural Inspector. See under *Health and Safety* in your telephone directory.

Control of Substances Hazardous to Health Regulations 1988 (COSHH)

The Agricultural and Horticultural Industries both use numerous substances which are hazardous, for example pesticides and fertilisers. Since the introduction of COSHH in 1988, a whole range of rules and regulations has been introduced, not just to help the agricultural industry but all industries that use hazardous substances.

About COSHH (general information – COSHH and pesticides will be dealt with separately)

COSHH are responsible for regulations which provide a framework for the control of substances at work which may be hazardous to health. These came into operation on 1st October 1989.

So what are the substances hazardous to health? Substances labelled very toxic, toxic, harmful, irritant or corrosive, and harmful micro-organisms, and also dusty, fume-producing or other materials which could harm people's health. Employers and the self-employed must make an adequate assessment of the risks from hazardous substances and decide on the control measures. This assessment should take the form of a considered assessment of the substances present in the workplace. The following questions will need to be asked:

1. Which substances are used in the workplace?
2. What are the possible harmful effects?
3. Where are the substances used, handled or stored?
4. Who may be exposed to them and for how long?
5. How can such exposure be prevented or controlled?

Anyone who may be affected by a hazardous substance must be told about the assessment.

To help control or prevent exposure, COSHH list the following control measures (in order of priority):

1. Substitute the substance with a safer alternative.
2. Introduce technical or engineering methods for controlling exposure.
3. Reduce exposure by following safe systems of work.

If these methods do not give adequate control, then, in addition, provide suitable protective clothing.

Pesticides

Legal controls on the use of pesticides to safeguard people and the environment were introduced on the 6th October 1986 and have come into effect progressively since then.

After 1st January 1989 the full system of approvals and consents which controls the use of pesticides was in force.

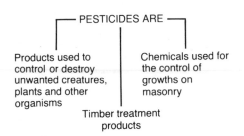

PESTICIDES ARE

Products used to control or destroy unwanted creatures, plants and other organisms

Timber treatment products

Chemicals used for the control of growths on masonry

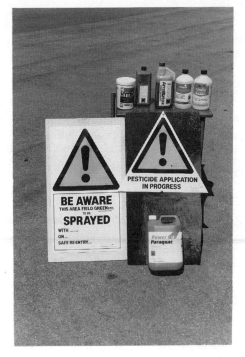

Pesticides

Buying Pesticides

Only pesticides which have been approved may now be advertised, sold or supplied in the UK. As part of the approval process, each product is given an approval number and conditions of use intended to ensure it is safe when used properly.

Every pesticide is assigned to a field of use which limits how it may be used, for example, agricultural, horticulture or forestry. The fields of use, product approval number and conditions of use are all given on the label. The following are statutory conditions and must always be observed:

- fields of use
- crops on which the product may be used
- maximum dose rate
- maximum number of treatments
- any limitation of area to be treated
- latest time for application
- operator protection
- environmental protection.

The label may also give additional advisory information which users are encouraged to follow.

COSHH and Pesticides

Most pesticides are covered by COSHH and can be easily identified by the risk symbol on the label.

A few do not have risk symbols, but they are covered by COSHH if they are in the list of occupational exposure limits set by the Health and Safety Executive – for example, benomyl. COSHH do not replace The Control of Pesticides Regulations 1986 (COPR), the two sets of regulations must be used together.

Pesticides

Q How will I know which pesticides I use are subject to COSHH?
A Most pesticides are covered and can be easily identified by the risk symbol on the label:

TOXIC / VERY TOXIC   CORROSIVE   HARMFUL / IRRITANT

Examples of COSHH risk symbols

> **! !   REMEMBER**
>
> COSHH are primarily aimed at protecting people at work. COPR cover creatures, plants and the environment, as well as human health.

Storage of Pesticides

Wholesale and retail stores are subject to controls under the regulations. Once pesticides have been delivered to an agricultural or horticultural holding, the occupier has the responsibility to take all reasonable precautions to ensure that they are stored and transported so as to protect people and animals, and to safeguard the environment. Special care is needed to avoid water pollution. Every workplace should have a pesticide store large enough to hold the maximum capacity of pesticides likely to be kept at any one time. The store may be separate or within an existing building or may be a chest, bin or vault. In every case it must be:

- suitably sited
- of adequate capacity and construction
- designed to hold spillage
- properly lit and ventilated
- resistant against fire and frost
- designed so that containers can be safely stacked and moved in and out
- clearly marked
- kept locked, except when in use.

✳ FOR INTEREST

If you have some pesticide in store and a safer alternative is now available, then provided the pesticide is still approved you can use it. However, change to the safer product at the first opportunity.

The Use of Pesticides

Only approved products may be used.

Everyone who uses a pesticide must be competent to do so, and employers must provide their workers with sufficient instruction and guidance to ensure that products are used safely, efficiently and humanely.

Safe and competent use of pesticides involves a careful evaluation of possible problems. Matters which need to be considered include:

- selection of the product
- how to comply with the conditions of approval
- correct protective clothing
- how to avoid spray drift
- how to avoid damage to the environment
- the need to warn neighbours and others who may be affected.

✳ FOR INTEREST

Practical guidance on the safe use of pesticides is given in the draft *Code of Practice: The Agricultural and Commercial. Horticulture Use of Pesticides*, which is published by the Ministry of Agriculture, Fisheries and Food.

Pesticide Training

Thorough training is vital if pesticides are to be used safely. This is not just good practice, it is a legal requirement. Formal training is frequently essential, but in all cases a person using pesticides must reach a minimum standard of competence.

Effective training can achieve this standard by a combination of instruction, practice and assessment. It is an employer's duty under the Health and Safety at Work Act 1974 to instruct, inform, train and supervise his/her employees.

Certificates of Competence

Anyone born later than 31st December 1964 who uses pesticides approved for agricultural use and anyone who uses them in the course of a commercial service must hold a Certificate of Competence by 1st January 1989 (or after) unless working under the direct and personal supervision of a Certificate holder. Certificates are issued by the National Proficiency Test Council (NPTC). 'Commercial service' includes not only contractors but also anyone who applies a pesticide to land which is not owned or occupied by him/herself or his/her employer.

Operators should be trained to:

- select the correct equipment for the work to be done
- adjust, calibrate and operate equipment safely
- carry out routine maintenance to manufacturers' instructions
- identify and rectify common faults
- know which faults need specialist attention
- clean and store equipment properly
- use and maintain the correct protective clothing and equipment
- clean protective items which are contaminated
- store the cleaned items.

✳ FOR INTEREST

The Poisonous Substances in Agriculture Regulations 1984 require that no employee should be allowed to work on scheduled operations unless he or she is thoroughly trained in the necessary precautions and is adequately supervised. This also applies to the self-employed.

‼ REMEMBER

Additional provisions for the safe use of pesticides are contained in the Food and Environment Protection Act (FEPA) 1985 and those requirements for training contained in Regulations made under this Act must be observed. You will be fined if you break the law.

Disposal of Pesticides

By careful estimation of the amounts needed, a user should avoid building up stocks of leftover pesticides. Similarly, correct measurement of the amount of spray mixed in the tank will avoid surplus dilute spray being left once a field has been treated.

However, some disposal of unwanted pesticides in the form of tank washings will often be necessary. For information on the disposal of pesticides you should refer to: 'Pesticides Code of Practice for the Safe Use of Pesticides on Farms and Holdings', published by the Ministry of Agriculture, Fisheries and Food (MAFF) and the Health and Safety Commission (HSC) (Chapter 5 Disposal of Pesticide Waste).

Pesticide Contamination

People working with pesticides should take care to avoid risks not only to themselves and fellow workers but also to the general public and the environment. If contamination does occur, then you should be trained in emergency action to include, where appropriate, decontamination procedures and in the case of suspected poisoning, where to get specialist help.

> **✳ FOR INTEREST**
>
> The Health and Safety Executive (HSE) produced a small leaflet entitled *Poisoning by Pesticides, First Aid*. This leaflet is available free of charge from the HSE office.

Pesticide 'User' Records

Pesticide training should also include the need for appropriate records to be kept and maintained; the correct procedures for storing, handling and mixing pesticides; and the disposal of empty containers. COSHH also require that a record of safety checks on engineering controls and respirators should be kept. Any monitoring of exposure or health surveillance must also be recorded.

Health surveillance involves a whole range of possibilities, from simply keeping a register to introducing periodical medical examinations or even blood testing, depending on the level of risk.

> **✳ FOR INTEREST**
>
> Health surveillance is only necessary when there is doubt that the exposure of the worker to the potentially harmful substance cannot be satisfactorily controlled, and in consequence the worker's health may be affected.

Safety at Work

Safety and Grasscutting

There is a wide range of grasscutting machinery available today which means that we can select the machine to suit specific requirements. Grasscutting machines are basically of two types:

1. Cylinder mowers (pedestrian or tractor mounted)
2. Rotary mowers (pedestrian or tractor mounted).

Ride-on rotary mower

Before you use any machine, it is wise to read the instruction book and make yourself familiar with all the controls.

Pre-start Checks of Pedestrian-operated Machines

1. Check that all moving parts are in good working order (disengage spark plug when checking cutting parts)
2. Check that all blades are secure
3. Check fuel (or fuel oil mix on two-stroke engines)
4. Check oil level (four-stroke engines have a separate oil sump)
5. Check on/off switch
6. Check lubrication and moving parts

Lifting and Carrying

Lifting and carrying can, if not done properly, lead to ruptures, strains and back injuries which may lay you up for weeks, even months. Mechanical aids have done much to lighten manual tasks within the horticultural industry, but there are still jobs which require considerable physical effort – lifting bags of compost for example.

Some injuries are caused by trying to move excessive weights but many are due to the failure to use the right method.

In all situations where lifting or carrying is necessary, it is better to use a mechanical method.

! ! REMEMBER

Be trained in the operation of any machine you are likely to use. Proper training in the use and application of machines should reduce potential hazards.

TIP

Before mowing an area, walk over it and check for debris/obstacles. This will make your mowing more efficient and less hazardous.

! ! REMEMBER

Safe lifting is a skill. It is much easier to lift a heavy weight from the ground if the strain is taken by your powerful leg and thigh muscles rather than by your back and abdomen.

Protective Clothing and Equipment

Area protected	Clothing/Equipment	Relevant British Standard
Head	Industrial Safety Helmet – hard hat to protect head from blows. Accessories include thermal liners, chinstrap and mounts for other protective equipment. Examples are ear muffs, visors and cap lamps.	BS5240
Eyes	Spectacles, Goggles, Visors – various grades protect against impact, dust, liquid splashes and droplets, gases/vapours and molten metal splash.	BS2092
Lungs	Respirators – fitted with a replaceable filter to remove harmful dusts from the inhaled air.	BS2091
	Disposable filtering facepiece respirators designed to give protection against harmful dusts for a limited period.	BS6016
Body	Jackets, Coats, Trousers, Coveralls, Overalls etc. – a wide variety of materials and styles to protect against general soiling, bad weather, dangerous chemicals, extreme temperatures, non-ionising radiations etc.	BS6408
	High Visibility Jackets, Waistcoats, Belts – make those working or passing near vehicles highly conspicuous. Aprons, gaiters, arm guards, knee-pads etc. – design to resist penetration by sharp objects, protect against cuts etc. or pressure (such as kneeling).	BS6629
Hands	Gloves, Gauntlets, Mitts – to protect hands and wrists from cuts, abrasions, hazardous fluids, hot and cold objects and bad weather.	BS1651 (does not cover the whole range)
Feet	Safety Boots, Wellingtons, Shoes – a wide range to protect the toes against crushing, soles against sharp objects, ankles, Achilles' tendon and top of leg against blows; keep feet dry and warm, and prevent slipping.	BS1870 (does not cover the whole range)

Remember, employers should provide clothing as necessary as part of a safe system of work, and ensure that it is used and properly maintained. Employees are required to co-operate with their employers in choosing, using and caring for protective clothing, and in reporting loss or damage.

Caring for Protective Clothing

1. Clean and wash after use.
2. Inspect regularly to ensure it is in good condition.
3. Make sure it is stored and dried properly.
4. Replace defective clothing and ensure that replacement stocks are available.

Some of the Hazards in the Horticultural Workplace

The following hazards do lead to many injuries at work:

Hazard	Example
Falls	off ladders, from machines, rooftops
Tractors	overturning, dismounting on the move
General machinery	lack of guards, lubricating or making adjustments while the machine is moving, poor maintenance
Noise	tractors without cabs, chainsaws, strimmers, hedge-cutters
Disease	tetanus, dermatitis
Chemicals	pesticide usage
Fire	fuels, chemicals
Electricity	overhead lines, poor maintenance, trailing leads, faulty wiring
Strains	incorrect lifting, carrying heavy weights

!! **REMEMBER**

Training and following the safe systems of work can effectively reduce hazards.

Accidents

An accident is an unplanned or uncontrolled event which many people associate with fate or just bad luck. It is a fact that the vast majority of accidents are caused by some form of human error.

!! **REMEMBER**

All accidents have a consequence – it may be a near miss, damage to property, injury or even death.

Accident Prevention

1. Know the safe system of work.
2. Ensure safety equipment, guards and protective clothing are used and adequately maintained.
3. Wear the correct protective clothing.
4. Follow manufacturers' instructions.
5. Be adequately trained for the job.
6. Study relevant information.
7. Carry out the job according to safe procedures.
8. Report any damage immediately.
9. Store all equipment carefully.

The information on Health and Safety given in this chapter has only been a brief summary. There is a wealth of information available on the subject; such information is produced in easy-to-read guides and booklets (many are free of charge) which are obtainable from:

1. Health and Safety Offices
   (look in the telephone book under *Health and Safety Executive*)
2. The Local Agricultural Inspector
3. The Local National Farmers' Union
4. The Agricultural Training Board

 TIP

Further advice on Health and Safety can also be obtained from manufacturers and suppliers, local safety groups, safety consultants and safety magazines.

THE HORTICULTURE INDUSTRY

Size

The UK Horticulture Industry is very large and, like many other industries, its huge expansion is a sign of its continuing success.

The industry has many sectors and sub-sectors which represent specialist areas in both professional and amateur terms. Professionally it is an industry that encompasses two distinct divisions, namely Commercial and Amenity.

Amenity view

Commercial Horticulture

Field Vegetables

Most commercial growers produce field vegetables, but many see themselves as farmers and as part of the agriculture industry. The importance of field vegetable growing cannot be over-emphasised. Although field vegetable crops are grown all over the UK, certain counties or parts of the UK are noted for their production of group or specific crops. This is a large and successful sector which has readily grasped new technology through improved mechanisation, but it has in some ways been a victim of its own success. Because the drilling, treating and harvesting of field vegetables have been greatly improved through mechanisation, craft employment has steadily declined. In contrast, employment in the marketing of field vegetables has increased.

Commercial view 1

Commercial view 2

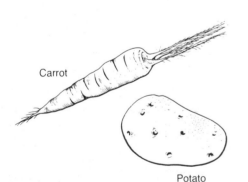

Carrot

Cabbage

Potato

Field-grown vegetables

Hardy Nursery Stock

This involves the production of essentially hardy plants – trees, shrubs, herbaceous, conifers, alpines and numerous other groups of plants – field grown and containerised. Although this sector has been established for a number of years, it has only relatively recently begun to expand. It is closely related to Amenity Horticulture because much of what it produces will be used by various Amenity sectors. It, too, is highly auto-mated, with computers being used widely for stock control, 'buying/selling' and invoicing.

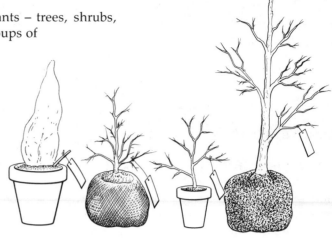

Container-grown hardy nursery stock

Fruit

Fruit production is a very old and established commercial sector, growing and marketing a wide range of crops. There are two groups of Fruit crops, top fruit (apples, pears, plums and cherries being the major examples) and soft fruit (raspberries, strawberries, gooseberries and blackcurrants representing the major crops). These two groups of fruit can also be subdivided into botanical groups, for example, raspberries are a cane fruit whereas plums are a stone fruit, and so on. In a similar way to field vegetable crops, fruit crops too have important growing areas across the UK, with particular commercially grown fruits being associated with particular counties. Sadly, the acreage of fruit crops has been in decline over recent years, however there has not been a drastic decline in overall production. In general terms, fruit-growing technology has made it possible to maximise fruit production on smaller areas of land.

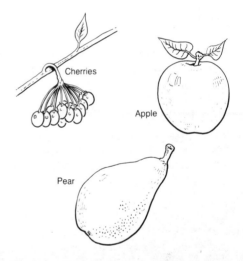

Commercially grown fruit

Protected Crops

Probably no other sector of the industry in recent years has developed and employed as much sophisticated technology for the control and monitor-ing of plant growth under protected environments. Today, the environ-ment in glasshouses and polythene structures can be controlled with the aid of computers. Here, plants enjoy ideal growing conditions from planting to marketing. Like many of the horticultural sectors, advanced technology has meant an expansion of this sector, but once again there has been a decline in craft employment because of this technology. However, opportunities within this sector are still reasonably good, particularly for horticulturists who have a degree of technical expertise.

A list of all the crops that could be grown under protected environments would fill several pages, but some of the more important are as follows:

- 'salad crops', such as tomatoes, cucumbers and lettuces
- 'flower crops', such as carnations, chrysanthemums and lilies
- 'seasonal crops', such as bedding plants
- 'houseplants', such as flowering and foliage pot plants.

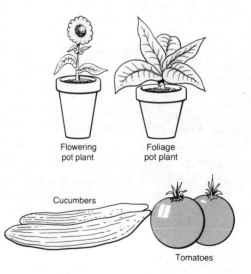

Protected crops

Amenity Horticulture

The main Amenity sectors are:
1. Local Authorities
2. Private
3. Landscape
4. Botanical Gardens.

Local Authorities

Local Authorities are responsible for much of our landscape. Within their control are public parks, recreation grounds, open spaces, street/verge plantings and gardens. As much of their work involves the management of sportsfields/turf areas and trees, detailed knowledge of Turfculture and Arboriculture is required. Local Authorities meet this demand by employing a wide range of specialist Amenity staff.

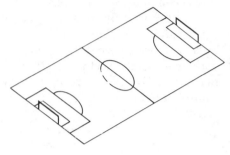

Sporting provision

Private

Essentially, private gardens are the large country houses and their estates. This is gardening on a grand scale where many horticultural specialisms are to be found. Many of these estates are today run and administered by the National Trust.

At the moment, the Amenity sector is enjoying a boom. It currently employs large numbers of people throughout the UK. With the expected increase in leisure time, horticultural provision will have a major role to play. Currently the employment possibilities within this sector are good – the industry will always need trained horticulturists.

Stately house and garden – Heath Hall, Wakefield (courtesy of Pirbic Northern Limited)

Landscape

This is an important sector of Amenity Horticulture which has expanded markedly over recent years. It includes the design, maintenance, construction and management of landscape features. Again, it is a diverse sector with numerous requirements which in turn offers employment to horticulturists with various specialist knowledge. By its very nature, landscape encompasses all the other specialist sectors of Amenity Horticulture in one form or another. Employment in this sector ranges from Garden Designers to Landscape Contractors.

A landscape scene

Botanical Gardens

Botanical gardens are to be found throughout the UK. Essentially they represent specialist gardens which may be state, council or privately owned. Other gardens which for various reasons are not strictly botanical, are also included in this category. Many of these have historical value.

Tropical plant specimens are often found in botanical gardens

Important Growing Areas in the UK

	Example of crop		Example of crop
Fruit		**Protected crops**	
Tayside	Raspberries	Lancashire	Tomatoes, lettuce
Worcestershire	Culinary apples, blackcurrants, plums	Humberside	Tomatoes, cucumbers, lettuce
Hampshire	Strawberries	Hertfordshire	Cucumbers
Kent	Dessert apples, cherries, culinary apples	Surrey	Lettuce
		Sussex	Carnations, chrysanthemums
		Nursery stock	
Vegetables		Highlands	Heathers, alpines
Yorkshire	Peas	Lincolnshire	General nursery stock
Lincolnshire	Onions, cabbage, asparagus, carrots	Norfolk	General nursery stock
Norfolk	Onions, asparagus, cabbage, carrots	Surrey	General nursery stock
Cambridgeshire	Celery	**Bulbs**	
Gloucestershire	Potatoes	Lincolnshire	General flower crops such as tulips and daffodils
Bedfordshire	Sprouts		
Cornwall	Winter cauliflowers	Cornwall	Anemones

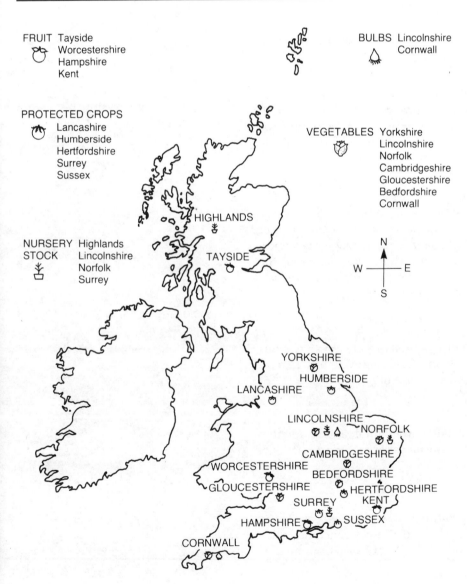

FRUIT Tayside
Worcestershire
Hampshire
Kent

BULBS Lincolnshire
Cornwall

PROTECTED CROPS
Lancashire
Humberside
Hertfordshire
Surrey
Sussex

VEGETABLES Yorkshire
Lincolnshire
Norfolk
Cambridgeshire
Gloucestershire
Bedfordshire
Cornwall

NURSERY STOCK
Highlands
Lincolnshire
Norfolk
Surrey

Map showing approximate positions of important growing areas of the UK

The Back-up Services (information courtesy of IOH)

The opportunities in this segment of the horticultural profession are considerable.

Advisory and Consultancy Work

The largest organisation is the Government's Agricultural Development and Advisory Service (ADAS) which employs qualified horticulturists to advise growers in England and Wales. There are equivalent services in Scotland and Northern Ireland. There is also an increasing number of private consultants working either in partnerships or as individuals, usually with specialist knowledge in a specific subject such as fruit growing, irrigation, soils etc.

Research

The Government also runs research and experimental stations covering the major horticultural crops. Much of this work requires people with graduate and post-graduate experience.

There are also several research stations run by commercial organisations.

Teaching and Lecturing

The teaching of horticultural and allied subjects ranges from rural science in schools to degree level in horticultural science at universities. Authorities are usually looking for applicants with a degree or high level diploma. Training Boards and Groups throughout the country also recruit qualified people.

Supplies and Services

The horticultural industry uses a vast range of inputs and services. Companies are frequently recruiting staff for posts which involve one or more of the following – selling, product management, technical advice, trial grounds work and product development. The actual nature of the businesses ranges from machinery to young plants, containers to glasshouses, fertilisers to packaging, agrochemicals to seeds.

Buyers

The large buyers of produce employ horticulturists to ensure that crops are grown according to their specification. Co-operatives too require trained people, as do processors and procurement organisations.

Communications

Full-time journalists are employed by the horticultural and gardening press. Many free-lancers work in a journalistic capacity for the national press, magazines, TV and radio.

Overseas

There is also a demand for trained horticulturists to work overseas. There are a number of UK-trained people working for companies concerned with crop production, in botanical gardens, and for the War Graves Commission throughout the world.

Training for Horticulture (Full-time Courses)

Both Amenity and Commercial Horticulture can be studied full-time.

National Certificate Horticulture (NCH) [One year course]

This craft level course combines practical and theoretical teaching and is available in a range of specialist options. NCH courses are offered by numerous Colleges of Agriculture and Horticulture throughout the country.

Advanced National Certificate Horticulture (ANCH) [One year course]

An advanced craft level course which combines practical and theoretical teaching and is available in a range of specialist options. ANCH courses are offered by numerous Colleges of Agriculture and Horticulture throughout the country.

National Diploma (BTEC National Diploma in Horticulture) [Three year sandwich course]

An in-depth technician level course, available in a range of specialist options, being offered at many Colleges of Agriculture and Horticulture throughout the country.

Higher National Diploma (BTEC Higher National Diploma in Horticulture) [Three year sandwich course]

A horticultural technology course, available in a range of specialist options, being offered at numerous Colleges of Agriculture and Horticulture throughout the UK.

Bachelor of Science (BSc) [Three or four years]

A horticultural science course offered only by a few universities and colleges in the country.

Master of Science (MSc), Master of Philosophy (MPhil) and Doctor of Philosophy (PhD) [One to four years, depending on FT or PT studies]

Such courses are offered only by a few UK universities.

NOTE
(1) Examining bodies and course structures differ in Scotland.
(2) Full-time courses of study are also offered at the Botanical Gardens of Kew (London) and Edinburgh (Scotland) on a three year full-time basis.
(3) Master of Horticulture (Royal Horticultural Society), courses (PT/FT): a highly respected and much sought after qualification. The MHort(RHS) is the highest independent qualification in horticulture in the UK.

A stepping stone to:

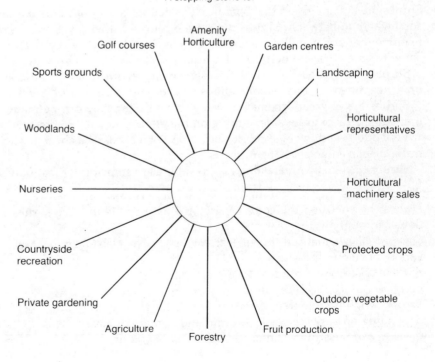

- Golf courses
- Amenity Horticulture
- Garden centres
- Sports grounds
- Landscaping
- Woodlands
- Horticultural representatives
- Nurseries
- Horticultural machinery sales
- Countryside recreation
- Protected crops
- Private gardening
- Outdoor vegetable crops
- Agriculture
- Forestry
- Fruit production

2 ORNAMENTAL HORTICULTURE AND DECORATIVE HORTICULTURE

Ornamental Horticulture and Decorative Horticulture are major parts of Amenity Horticulture; a garden can be greatly improved either by using different groups of plants or by using different garden features. For example, bedding plants are both ornamental and decorative, as is a rock garden.

There are many ways in which Ornamental Horticulture and Decorative Horticulture can be used. Here are some well known examples:

1. Shrubs
2. Herbaceous perennials
3. Bedding plants
4. Rock gardens
5. Containers.

Lawns are also considered Ornamental, but lawns and turfculture are considered as a separate item in the next chapter.

Rock garden – scree bed

Shrubs

Shrubs are a plant group that botanically is neither trees nor herbs but lies somewhere in between. Shrubs during the course of their lives will show features that are tree-like, for example, they are 'woody'. They will also show features that are herb-like, for example, fleshy or soft growth.

Shrubs are woody perennial bushy plants with many individual branches, often having two or more stems coming from ground level.

Shrubs are of great ornamental value to a garden; they can be planted individually or in groups depending on the effect you wish to create.

Very often we think of shrubs as being part of a border – a shrub border, being displayed as permanent plants.

Shrubs have many interesting features; here are some of the main ones.

Shape: various shapes or forms, horizontal or vertical.
Flowers: by choosing the correct varieties it is possible to have shrubs in flower throughout the year.
Coloured foliage: many different leaf colours are available, giving a good variety of colour and shape.
Autumn colour: vivid colours before leaf fall.
Evergreen: in leaf all year round.
Berries: brightly coloured, large or small clusters or individual berries depending on variety, giving autumn and winter colour.
Coloured bark: useful in winter to provide extra colour.

> **! ! REMEMBER**
>
> Shrubs can be Evergreen or Deciduous.

Shrub border

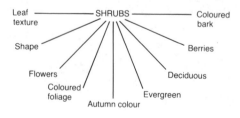
Shrub features

Shrub Checks

We have already seen that shrubs can provide a wide range of interesting features, however, to make the most of shrubs we need to ask ourselves what it is we require from them. Selecting shrubs therefore is not as simple as it might seem, and a number of checks should be carried out. For example:

1. *Check soil pH. Is it acid or alkaline?*
This is very important and something which can be done easily and quickly. Knowing whether your soil is acid or alkaline will decide just what shrubs you can or cannot grow. *Rhododendrons*, for example, prefer an acid soil and so should not be planted on an alkaline (limey) soil. Flowering currant (*Ribes*) however prefers alkaline soil.

2. *Is the planting site suitable for shrubs?*
Find out if the soil drains well; carry out some digging and see if the soil would benefit from an application of organic matter. Organic matter is very useful to a soil; it will help with drainage, aeration and add to the soil's fertility. If your planting site is exposed you will need to provide your plants with shelter; many shrubs suffer in exposed sites.

3. *Check your planting area for weeds.*
Perennial weeds could cause problems as they will compete for light, nutrients and space, which will mean your shrubs have a poor start. Perennial weeds can be controlled quite easily using various weedkillers of the translocated type. (Translocated weedkillers are taken in by the plant and moved around within it, killing both the foliage and root system.)

 TO DO

With the help of your tutor make a list of, and identify, five acid-loving plants and five alkaline-loving plants. How many did you know?

 TO DO

Make a soil pH test using a suitable pH testing kit. Make a diagram showing the materials and equipment you used.

Using Shrubs

Borders

Traditionally shrubs have been, and still are, grown in borders. Here they are planted either in groups, as individuals or as a combination of both. Planted in this way, shrubs can be very effective; however, if we are to obtain good results a great deal of thought needs to be put into the design of the border. A traditional border usually has as its backdrop a wall, fence or even a hedge.

Ideally the border should be designed to show off shrubs all year round, so that many of their distinctive features already described can be seen.

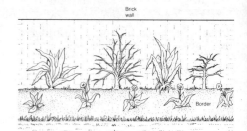

Traditional shrub border

Double Digging

This is the cultivation of soil to two spits depth. The second spit is forked and a suitable manure or compost is worked in.

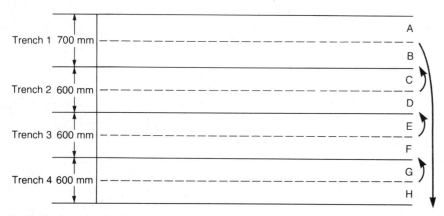

Double digging – the view from above

1. Remove the soil from trench 1 (A + B); this is usually transported to the end of the plot and used to fill in the last trench.
2. Turn trench 2 (C + D) into trench 1 (A + B); this operation is continued until you reach the end of the plot.

! !   REMEMBER

For a one-sided shrub border you need to have tall plants towards the back, medium-sized plants in the middle, and small plants towards the front.

TIP

If your border is to be a permanent one, double digging will be better than single digging. This will give your plants a better start and help their establishment.

Island Beds

These beds are probably best described as borders set within a grassed area. Such beds are often used in parks and gardens and can be used to accommodate various plants other than shrubs. Where they are to be used for shrubs, they will only be effective if the bed is planted up according to the size and spread of the shrub.

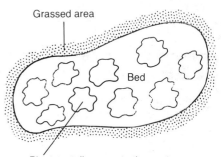

Plants – taller ones to the centre, smaller ones to the outside

Island bed – all round viewing

Ground Cover

Many shrub species are suitable for use as ground cover plants. These are very useful in keeping down weeds, and are therefore useful in maintenance programmes. Ground cover shrubs are nowadays used extensively in landscape plantings; often they are quick to establish and easy to grow.

TIP

If possible, choose evergreens for ground cover plants. This will give colour all year round and so help to maintain an interesting garden.

Walls, Fences and Trellises

There are many shrubs that are regarded as being wall shrubs, for example, Winter Jasmine (*Jasminum nudiflorum*), and there are those that are known as climbers, for example, Virginia Creeper (*Parthenocissus*). Shrubs that fall into either of these groups can be grown up or on a wide variety of supports such as walls, fences and trellises.

Some shrubs do not need any artificial support such as trellis or wires, since they are adapted for climbing using a variety of techniques. Virginia Creeper (*Parthenocissus*) is able to climb a vertical wall using small suction pads, others like Ivy (*Hedera*) use tiny roots which will grow into brickwork and so give anchorage to the plant. Some shrubs climb by using a twining growth pattern; they will wrap themselves around free-standing supports such as a trellis or fence post. Honeysuckle (*Lonicera*) is a good example. Some shrubs climb using twining leaf stems; they clasp the support and proceed to climb it. *Clematis* is a typical example.

Some shrubs, although regarded as climbers, do need a good deal of support if they are to be successful. Winter Jasmine will make a good wall shrub provided it is given both support and training. This is done using wires pulled across anchor points or supports across the face of the wall. The plant is then able to climb the wall and is secured by tying in branches at regular intervals onto the wires.

 SAFETY

When planting wall shrubs, make sure your soil level is below the damp course level if planting up to the house.

! ! **REMEMBER**

Before you plant a climber, know its ultimate size and pruning requirements. You do not want to end up with the plant in the wrong place.

 TIP

When preparing supports on walls, use galvanised wire as it is non-rusting. Also make sure the wires are firm and taut before tying in.

Formal Gardens

Probably the most popular shrub used for formal gardens is the Rose (*Rosa*). Of the many different groups of Rose available, the large flowered (Hybrid Tea) and cluster flowered roses (Floribunda) have been and still are used extensively in parks and gardens. Either group is well suited to being grown in formal beds and both respond to good maintenance.

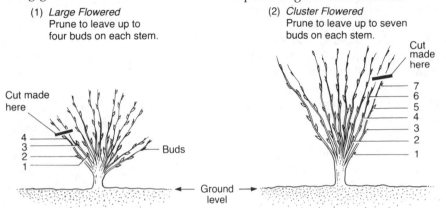

(1) *Large Flowered*
Prune to leave up to four buds on each stem.

Cut made here
4
3
2
1
Buds

(2) *Cluster Flowered*
Prune to leave up to seven buds on each stem.

Cut made here
7
6
5
4
3
2
1

← Ground level →

The reason why a greater number of buds are left on the cluster flowered roses is because they are bigger plants.

Pruning of large flowered and cluster flowered roses

Rose bed

Specific Beds (Informal)

Some shrubs are best grown in association with each other in order to gain the maximum effect. Heaths and Heathers are perfect examples of this. Together they are known as Heathers and are often grown with their own kind in beds. In more recent years they have become widely used with dwarf conifers to produce a very good garden and ornamental feature. Although some heathers are lime tolerant, the majority are acid-loving plants and will therefore benefit from prepared beds of peaty compost. There is a whole range of cultivars available today and these are now an important part of the Nursery Stock industry. By combining the right varieties, heather borders can be in flower all year round. Also, many varieties are valued for their foliage colour which will also give year-round interest. In the main, Heathers are small ground cover plants although some of the Tree Heaths (*Erica* species) can reach several metres in height.

 TO DO

What is the difference between Large Flowered Roses (Hybrid Tea) and Cluster Flowered Roses (Floribundas)? Make a list of ten examples of each. Note the colour range.

 TIP

Pruning Roses – March
- Remove dead, diseased and dying wood.
- Remove weak growth.
- Remove crossing branches.
- Prune to an outward-facing bud.
- Large Flowered (Hybrid Tea) Roses are pruned to 2–4 buds (see diagram).
- Cluster Flowered (Floribunda) Roses are pruned to 6–7 buds (see diagram).

 TO DO

Make a list of four of the following:

(1) Winter-flowering heathers
(2) Spring-flowering heathers
(3) Summer-flowering heathers
(4) Autumn-flowering heathers
(5) Lime-tolerant heathers
(6) Coloured foliage heathers

 USEFUL TERMS

Variety generally indicates that this form has originated in the wild (wild varieties).
Cultivars are generally those selected varieties that are maintained and grown in cultivation.

Hedges

Both deciduous and evergreen shrubs can be used to make a hedge. Hedges are very useful, and here are some of their functions:

1. as shelter
2. to give privacy
3. to separate or enclose
4. to mark boundaries
5. to act as a backdrop for other plantings
6. as barriers.

Hedges can be either formal or informal. Formal hedges are clipped at set times, generally kept neat and tidy, and in the main do not flower. Informal hedges are allowed to flower and are pruned sparingly. Some formal hedge examples are:

Laurel (*Prunus*) – evergreen
Beech (*Fagus*) – deciduous
Spotted Laurel (*Aucuba*) – evergreen

Some informal hedge examples are:

Escallonia – evergreen
Forsythia – deciduous
Flowering Currant (*Ribes*) – deciduous

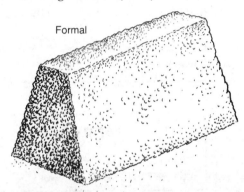

Formal

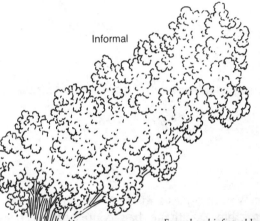

Informal

Formal and informal hedges

The frequency at which hedges are cut depends on the following:

1. Type of plant
2. Position in the garden
3. The standard of maintenance required
4. Whether the hedge is formal or informal.

The time of year to cut hedges will vary depending on plant species and also whether it is formal or informal. When choosing a hedging plant, particularly one that is suited to formal use, take into account the number of times you will need to cut it in a year. Privet (*Ligustrum*), for example, will need to be cut at regular intervals from spring through to autumn.

 TIP

If large leaved evergreens are used for a hedge, they should be pruned using secateurs otherwise half leaves will be left which will turn brown and die. Laurel (*Prunus*) should be pruned in this way.

Other Uses

Because shrubs as a group contain a very wide variety of plants, their uses in Amenity Horticulture are limitless. Shrubs can be used in all types of gardens such as rock gardens, woodland gardens, gardens for the blind, gardens for the disabled, or in association with other plants in a mixed border.

Shrub Planting

Once the land has been prepared using various hand tools or pedestrian-operated machinery and all perennial weed has been removed, planting should be the next stage. However, existing weather conditions should be taken into account and you should not work the soil if it is waterlogged or too hard.

Shrubs are available for planting in one of three forms. These are:

1. *Bare rooted plants*. These are widely available for sale and planting in the dormant season. If plants cannot be planted quickly, they should be heeled-in until they can be planted.

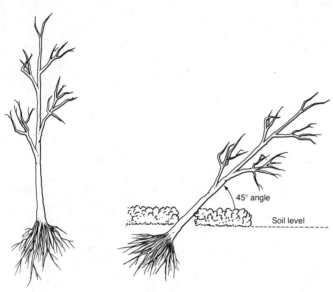

Heeling-in bare rooted plants

2. *Containerised plants*. Various sizes and types of container are used for shrubs, ranging from thin polythene bag containers to heavier and stronger rigid plastic containers. The advantage of growing a plant in a container is that it can be planted at any time of the year, provided that weather conditions are suitable.

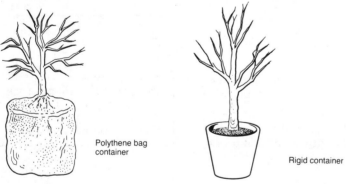

Containers for hardy plants

3. *Root-balled plants*. This is the form often used for many species of field grown hardy nursery stock; *Rhododendrons* for example are often presented in this way. It effectively produces a loose type of container; hessian sacking and similar materials are used for root-balling plants.

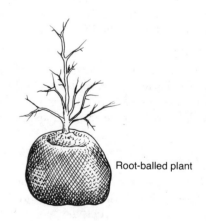

Root-balling plants is useful for field-grown nursery stock

! ! REMEMBER

Remove polythene bag, rigid and root ball materials prior to planting. If this is not done, you will constrict the root system.

❀ TIP

Count out the number of containerised plants you have to plant. At the end of your planting you should have the same number of empty containers on the surface.

✳ FOR INTEREST

If for some reason you are not able to plant containerised plants for some time, you will need to keep them well watered and give them an occasional feed.

Containerised plants dry out quickly, particularly in warm weather.

△ SAFETY

Wear the necessary protective footwear when planting.

When planting shrubs, make sure that you do not plant them below their previous line of planting, to do this could harm the plant.

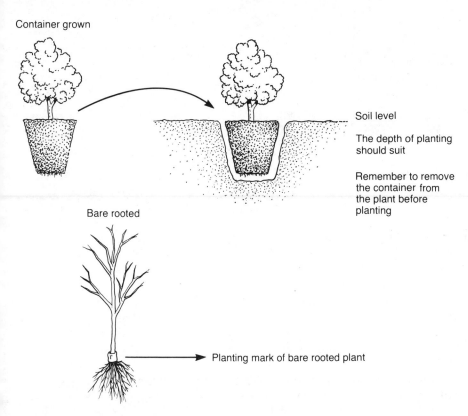

Container grown

Soil level

The depth of planting should suit

Remember to remove the container from the plant before planting

Bare rooted

Planting mark of bare rooted plant

Planting container-grown and bare rooted plants

For the average bare-rooted or containerised shrub a planting pit of about 300 mm × 300 mm × 300 mm is about right; these distances can be reduced for smaller shrubs, for example Heathers. Select the appropriate tools for planting. This will largely be determined by the size of the plant. You may wish to grade your plants before planting, and mark out your planting positions on the bed. This can be done using either canes or sand. In any event, planting positions should ideally be taken from your pre-prepared plan of the site. Plant your shrubs, label them if appropriate and water them in. Once all the planting is done, tidy up the bed or site.

Mulching

To mulch a shrub bed or border is to place a layer of bulky organic material, for example, well rotted farm yard manure, over the soil surface and around plants. Care must be taken not to mulch right up to the main stem of the plant as this might lead to scorching. An ideal time to apply a mulch is early summer, for example, May; this will conserve moisture, cool the plant's roots and help suppress weeds. Mulches are therefore a good maintenance aid.

! !   REMEMBER

A plan of the site will make planting easier, as it will confirm planting depths and distance apart of plants in the bed.

TIP

A pre-planting fertiliser will help the shrubs to establish themselves more quickly. This is often applied as a top dressing and worked in the soil before planting.

▶ ▶ ▶   TO DO

Make a sketch plan of a rectangular shrub border 6 m × 3 m. Assume you have a red brick wall to a height of 3 m at the back of the border. A pathway of 1.2 m runs at both ends and in front of the border. Remember the principles of planting such a border, mentioned earlier in this chapter.

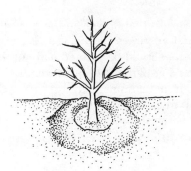

A mulch placed at the base of a shrub – note that the mulch is clear of the stem

Mulching plants

Maintaining Shrubs

During the first year after planting:

(a) replace dead or dying shrubs
(b) prune damaged shrubs
(c) attend to watering, particularly over the summer months
(d) control weeds, either by mechanical or chemical means.

In the following years:

(a) continue weed control
(b) apply mulch
(c) prune as required
(d) feed, by applying suitable fertilisers.

Pruning Shrubs

This is a task that requires both knowledge and skill.

Without a knowledge of shrub types and the necessary pruning skills, you will find it difficult to prune shrubs correctly. Both knowledge and skill can be built up by experience, and attendance at training courses which cover the pruning of shrubs. For the purposes of pruning, shrubs fall into two groups: evergreens and deciduous.

Evergreens: Generally shrubs which are evergreen and grown as individual specimens do not require a great deal of pruning. Their pruning is aimed at keeping a reasonable shape to the plant.

Deciduous: Shrubs that lose their leaves in autumn are known as deciduous. This very large group of shrubs, which contains a great number of species, is pruned according to the wood on which flowers are produced. This group can be further subdivided, but the two main groups are as follows:

(a) *Shrubs that flower on the current season's growth*
Examples are

> Buddleia
> Rosa
> Hypericum

(b) *Shrubs that flower on the previous year's growth*
Examples are

> Forsythia
> Jasminum
> Ribes

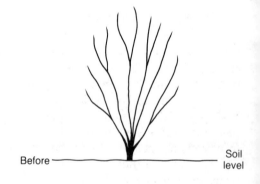

Shrubs that flower on the current season's growth can be pruned at two different times of the year according to species. For example, *Buddleia davidii* should be pruned early in the year, cutting hard back the previous year's growth. This shrub will then flower on the current season's growth from mid summer onwards.

Pruning of this shrub is carried out in February or March

Pruning Buddleia davidii

Winter Jasmine should be pruned soon after flowering, which would be in early spring; it would then flower in winter on the previous year's growth.

The Pruning Operation

Firstly look at and consider the type of shrubs you are to prune. Make a note of their size, spread and position, and above all make sure you know the method of pruning for each shrub. To help you decide how to carry out the pruning operation, the following points will make a useful guide:

1. Identify the shrubs that require pruning.
2. Select the right tools for the job.
3. Remove from all shrubs the 3 'D's: (a) Dead wood
                                          (b) Diseased wood
                                          (c) Dying wood.
4. Identify on each shrub, where appropriate, the flowering wood.
5. Decide method of pruning as appropriate to the shrub.
6. Prune the shrub accordingly.
7. After pruning, the shrub should be left with a good shape (this will depend on the type of shrub relative to the pruning method).
8. If the shrubs are of the climbing group, then some training will be needed.
9. Remove prunings and any other debris from site after pruning.
10. You must leave the site clean and tidy, and remember to rake out your footprints if you have been pruning shrubs in a border. Tools and equipment should be cleaned and returned to their store.
11. At all times, make sure you are working to and using safe practices.

 SAFETY

You may need to use ladders when pruning large shrubs. Make sure you follow the safe code of practice associated with the use of ladders. Ask your tutor!

 TO DO

With the help of your tutor, make up a list of shrubs that should be pruned at different times of the year. In your list, note whether your shrubs are grown for their flowers only or if they have some other interesting feature which requires them to be pruned at that time.

Shrubs – Examples

Shrubs suitable for a small garden:
1. *Berberis thunbergii 'Atropurpurea'*
2. *Hebe pinguifolia 'Pagei'*
3. *Lavandula spica.*

Shrubs with variegated foliage:
1. *Griselinia littoralis variegata*
2. *Euonymus fortunei*
3. *Sambucus racemosa 'Plumosa Aurea'.*

Shrubs for early flowering:
1. *Hamamelis mollis*
2. *Jasminum nudiflorum*
3. *Mahonia japonica.*

Shrubs for spring flowering:
1. *Berberis x stenophylla*
2. *Cytisus x kewensis*
3. *Spiraea x arguta.*

Shrubs for early summer flowering:
1. *Weigela florida 'Bristol Ruby'*
2. *Ceanothus 'Gloire de Versailles'*
3. *Senecio greyii.*

Shrubs for mid/late summer flowering:
1. *Buddleia davidii*
2. *Hypericum androsaemum*
3. *Potentilla fruticosa 'Katherine Dykes'.*

Shrubs for autumn flowering:
1. *Ceanothus x burkwoodii*
2. *Caryopteris x clandonensis*
3. *Hebe 'Autumn Glory'.*

Shrubs for ground cover:
1. *Erica species*
2. *Hypericum calycinum*
3. *Pachysandra terminalis.*

Shrubs which are evergreen:
1. *Camellia japonica*
2. *Garrya elliptica*
3. *Viburnum tinus.*

Shrubs for autumn colour:
1. *Acer palmatum*
2. *Cotinus coggygria*
3. *Viburnum opulus.*

Shrubs with berries:
1. *Cotoneaster horizontalis*
2. *Pernettya mucronata*
3. *Pyracantha coccinea 'Lalandii'.*

Shrubs which have coloured stems or barks:
1. *Cornus alba 'Sibirica'*
2. *Kerria japonica*
3. *Salix alba 'Chermesina'.*

Shrubs for planting at seaside regions:
1. *Elaeagnus pungens*
2. *Hippophae rhamnoides*
3. *Tamarix species.*

Shrubs suitable for acid conditions:
1. *Calluna species*
2. *Gaultheria shallon*
3. *Rhododendron species.*

Shrubs suitable for alkaline conditions:
1. *Buddleia species*
2. *Forsythia species*
3. *Rosmarinus species.*

Shrubs for shady areas:
1. *Camellia species*
2. *Rhododendron species*
3. *Skimmia species.*

Shrubs suitable for dry conditions:
1. *Cistus species*
2. *Genista species*
3. *Lavandula species.*

Shrubs suitable for formal hedges:
1. *Ligustrum ovalifolium*
2. *Lonicera nitida*
3. *Cotoneaster simonsii.*

Shrubs suitable for informal hedges:
1. *Forsythia species*
2. *Escallonia species*
3. *Rosa species.*

 TO DO

For all the plants listed, make a note of their different flower colour and the number of weeks that each plant is expected to remain in flower.

Herbaceous Perennials

This is a group of plants that produce herbaceous (soft fleshy) growth above ground each year, coming from a persistent rootstock below ground level. Unless the individual plant is winter flowering, the majority of plants within this group die back to ground level in the winter.

Herbaceous perennials are used widely in Amenity Horticulture, particularly in gardens. Such plants have a great ornamental and decorative value; there is a very large variety of plants to choose from, ranging from ground cover plants to plants that will need staking and tying.

Traditionally, herbaceous perennials have been grown in borders or island beds with much of their interest being in the summer months when the majority of herbaceous plants flower. However, while they are still grown in this way, these plants do have a number of other uses.

Here are the functions of herbaceous perennials:

1. In the traditional herbaceous border
2. In island beds
3. In mixed borders (usually as gap fillers between shrubs)
4. In specific gardens such as woodland gardens or rock gardens
5. In bog gardens (a number of species, for example primulas, prefer moist conditions)
6. In flower gardens – here they can be grown as a cut flower crop.

Herbaceous bed

Growing Herbaceous Perennials

Many herbaceous plants will make a great deal of growth during the year, however some of this growth could cause problems at the height of their growing season if they have been planted too close together. Herbaceous plants need good light and a good air circulation if they are to grow well. Soil type and the condition of the soil are other important factors to consider; some plants such as *Phlox species* will do better in a rich soil, while others such as *Stachys* do better in poor soil. Soil pH is important; Border Pinks for example require chalk, but some of the Poppies prefer acid conditions.

Some plants require shade and are at home in a woodland garden, for example, Hellebores.

Planting Herbaceous Perennials

The following are the main points to consider.

If possible, avoid heavy clay soils or soils that are poorly drained, unless you can improve such soils. It is important that herbaceous plants are not located in such a way that their crowns hold water for long periods of time. Anticipatation of this problem avoids crown rotting. The easiest way to achieve this is to plant slightly proud of the soil, but remember to plant deep enough to cover the roots.

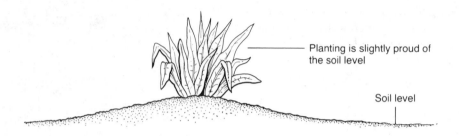
How to plant perennials

Before any planting starts, particularly if you are to plant a new border or bed, a good deal of planning needs to be done. You need to consider the type of plants you want in relation to how you are going to show them off. For example, your border would be best sited east/west, which means it should face south. However, if the border needs shelter, you will only be able to view it from one side; but generally this is not a problem needing consideration. Where possible, try to avoid north/east borders as they tend to stay cold early in the season.

 TIP

Scale is an important feature of the border. Generally the wider the border is, then the longer it should be. Also the longer a border is, the better use you can make of your taller plants.

 TO DO

Make a scale drawing of a border 10 m × 4 m and use as many different herbaceous plants as you can. Take into account heights, colours and season of interest. Assume your border is east/west and is sheltered by a beech hedge 1.8 m high.

 **! !** **REMEMBER**

If your plants are to be put in either a border or island bed, some form of shelter will be needed. Herbaceous perennials are often damaged by winds.

! ! **REMEMBER**

Plant well in from the border's edge, particularly if your bed adjoins grass. Otherwise the plants could cause problems when the grass is mown.

 TIP

If planting in groups, try and use odd numbers. The effect is much better.

30

Planting Preparations

A good deal of bed preparation should be done before planting; the removal of all perennial weeds is essential. Ideally you should incorporate in the soil some organic material; for instance leafmould, farmyard manure or peat can be worked in when digging is carried out. A pre-planting base fertiliser such as bonemeal could also be incorporated. On a small scale, double digging could be carried out, however if your border is too big, mechanical cultivations offer a good alternative. Timing of cultivations and the interval to planting depend on soil type and planting season. For example, cultivations in autumn should present suitable planting conditions for the following spring. Yet if you were to plant in autumn, cultivations would be best carried out in spring or early summer.

Once all preparations have been carried out, planting can begin. Plant at the correct depths and firm-in as necessary. If your plants are to be labelled, the labels should be bold, clearly written and positioned for ease of viewing.

After planting, water each plant; and if the planting has been carried out in spring, a mulch can be applied. The bed should be left clean and tidy, and tools and equipment should be cleaned and returned to the store.

TIP

Unless your border has access to irrigation, do not plant on light soils early in the year. These soils often dry out in spring/early summer. You will have more success with spring plantings on heavier soils.

! ! REMEMBER

Herbaceous perennials that have been divided before planting can easily dry out. Therefore only lay out on the bed those plants that you can plant quickly. If too many are spread on the surface before planting, they will become damaged.

In the season following planting, the plants will benefit from a dressing of fertiliser; a nitrogen fertiliser will be especially useful to the plants. However, not all herbaceous plants require nitrogen. Lupins, which are a legume, for example, fix their own nitrogen, while *Artemesia* requires little nitrogen.

! ! REMEMBER

Nitrogen fertiliser could cause an excess of leafy growth unless phosphate and potash is also given.

Maintenance of Herbaceous Perennials

Whether you are growing herbaceous plants in traditional borders, island beds or in mixed borders, they will all need regular maintenance. The following points should be considered:

1. Seasonal feeding – throughout the season the plants should be given small amounts of balanced fertilisers, particularly if they are on light soils.
2. Mulching – every spring/early summer, borders will benefit from mulching. Try to use different organic materials every year.
3. Weed control – this is a constant maintenance problem; regular hoeing or hand weeding of annual weeds is required. Keep a watchful eye for perennial weeds as very often they can be re-introduced into the border. Should they be missed, weeds will compete against plants for nutrients, light and water. While mulches will help with weed control, you may find it necessary to introduce selective herbicides.
4. Supports – the taller plants will need some support during the season. This can be done quite easily using a combination of canes and ties. Try to support your plants early and do not worry about the visual impact of the supports; they will be hidden as the plant develops through the season.
5. Dead heading – the removal of dead or dying flower heads is a continual process during a plant's flowering season.

SAFETY

When using herbicides with herbaceous plants, make sure you select the right types. Because herbaceous plants are soft and fleshy, they can be easily damaged. Ask your tutor for help in selecting herbicides for the herbaceous border.

✳ FOR INTEREST

Herbaceous plants grown in traditional borders will grow on for many years. However, your border would benefit from being re-planted, the plants being divided and moved at intervals of about 4 to 5 years. This form of renovation will help keep your border or bed in a good and healthy condition. You may wish to use some of your new plant divisions to start another border.

Herbaceous Perennials – Examples

The following list of herbaceous perennials is suitable for garden planting. Mixing colours in the border is a very good way of showing the plants off.

Name	Flower colour	Coloured foliage	Flowering season	Height (cm)
Achillea 'Moonshine'	Yellow		Early/mid summer	60–70
Anaphalis triplinervis	White		Late summer	24–45
Anchusa 'Pride of Dover'	Blue		Early summer	90–120
Aruncus sylvester	White		Early summer	120–150
Aster novi-belgii 'Fellowship'	Pink		Late summer	90–100
Bergenia 'Ballawley'	Rose pink		Early spring	30–40
Chrysanthemum maximum 'Wirral Supreme'	White		Mid summer	60–75
Coreopsis verticillata 'Grandiflora'	Yellow		Mid summer	35–60
Delphinium elatum 'Blue Nile'	Blue		Mid summer	150
Dicentra spectabilis	Pink/white		Early summer	30–60
Echinops ritro 'Taplow Blue'	Blue		Mid summer	120–130
Geranium endressii 'Wargrave variety'	Pink		Early/mid summer	30–40
Geum borisii 'Mrs. J. Bradshaw'	Crimson		Early summer	60
Heleborus orientalis	Purple		Winter	30–45
Incarvillea delavayi	Pink		Early summer	30–45
Kniphofia galpinii	Orange		Late summer	45–60
Lupin 'George Russell'	Pink		Early summer	90
Lychnis chalcedonica	Scarlet		Early/mid summer	100
Paeonia hybrids 'Victoria'	Crimson		Early summer	60–90
Phlox paniculata 'Eventide'	Mauve		Mid summer	60–90
Polemonium foliosissimum	Blue		Mid/late summer	60–75
Primula denticulata	Blue/pink		Early spring	20–30
Rudbeckia 'Goldsturm'	Yellow		Mid/late summer	60–70
Sedum 'Autumn Joy'	Pink		Late summer	35–50
Solidago 'Goldenmosa'	Yellow		Mid summer	60–90
Verbascum 'Mont Blanc'	White		Early/mid summer	100–120

Many Herbaceous perennials also exhibit foliage coloured other than green, which further adds to the attraction of the border.

Coloured foliage
Place a tick in this column of the table for those plants you consider to have coloured foliage (that is, other than green).

 TO DO

Make a list of 12 herbaceous plants that have foliage coloured other than green?

Bedding Plants

Bedding plants are made up of a number of different types of groups of plants. Before we look at bedding plants and their uses in more detail, we need to look more closely at these different botanical groups.

1. *Annuals*

By definition, an annual is a plant that can be grown from seed – growing, flowering, fruiting and seeding, and then dying all in one year. Annuals are of greatest interest in summer. They can be divided into two groups, as follows:

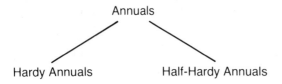

Hardy annuals are those plants that are sown outdoors in prepared beds or borders in the position in which they will flower. Very often hardy annuals are grown either in island beds or borders. Before any sowing is carried out the site should be thoroughly prepared, by incorporating some organic matter. This is an ideal job for the autumn. During winter, decide on the plants you wish to grow and make a plan drawing of your site. You will need to make sure you know the ultimate heights of your plants, tall plants being located to the centre and smaller plants towards the outside. Also, give careful consideration to your colour scheme and season of flowering; ideally you will want a border that flowers throughout the summer.

In spring, select appropriate tools and materials and prepare a seedbed on your site. Use sand or sawdust to mark out your drifts on the bed; in this way you can see where you are sowing and watch that it matches your plan. Regarding sowing, you have two alternatives: either broadcast sow, which means you simply scatter the seed over the area, or sow in short rows. Sowing in short rows gives you the advantage of knowing exactly where your seeds are when they germinate, as your seedlings will come up in straight lines.

Sowing Hardy Annuals in Drifts

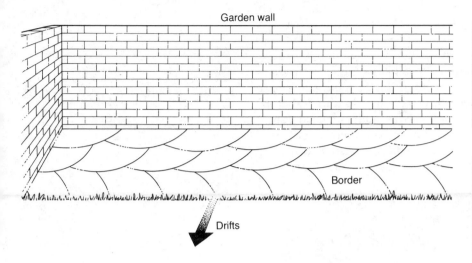

Sowing hardy annuals in drifts

 TO DO

With the help of a seed catalogue, design your own annual border. Assume your border measures 6 m × 3 m.

 TIP

The best time to sow your border/bed is about April/May. However, this will vary year to year depending on existing weather conditions.

! ! **REMEMBER**

Hardy annuals prefer light and well ventilated conditions. Try to give your plants a reasonable access to both.
Select your sites carefully.

△ **SAFETY**

When applying pesticide, make sure you have had the appropriate training.

 TIP

Hardy annuals can also be used in mixed borders, as gap fillers or in containers. You do not need a large border to grow them.

Weeding is made easier when planting is in straight lines inside the drifts, since any seedlings coming up between the rows have a good chance of being weeds. With the broadcast method of sowing, the identification of weed seedlings and plants is much more difficult. Each drift is sown with a different annual and labelled. Once germination has taken place the seedlings will need to be thinned out as appropriate. If staking and tying is necessary for some of your plants, remember to do this early.

Maintenance of Hardy Annuals

The maintenance of these plants is a continuous operation, and to keep your border/bed in good order the following points should be considered:

1. Weed control – hand weeding or hoeing.
2. Watering – depends on the season; in drought conditions, some watering will be needed.
3. Feeding – the plants will benefit from some feeding during the season; this can be done using granulated compound fertilisers.
4. Dead heading – the removal of old or dying flower heads.
5. Supports – tying or caning plant groups or individual plants as required.
6. Pest and disease control – apply appropriate pesticides as and when needed.

2. Half-hardy Annuals

Plants in this group are less hardy than the hardy annuals, and as such cannot be sown directly into beds or borders. Half-hardy annuals are sown under protection, usually glass, and are not planted out into their flowering position until the last of the frost has gone. Very often it is these annuals that are known as bedding plants. These plants are sown in trays or pots; after germination, they are pricked out and grown on, still under glass, until eventually they are hardened off, usually in cold frames, before finally being planted out. The range of half-hardy annuals is considerable, and they have now become an important part of the commercial industry.

The main use of these plants is in summer bedding schemes of public parks and gardens, private gardens and domestic gardens. They are very popular plants for summer flowering.

Summer bedding scheme

Half-hardy annuals have a large colour range, flowering period and size. Other uses of half-hardy annuals include:

1. In containers on patios
2. As gap fillers in shrub or mixed borders
3. In hanging baskets
4. In window boxes
5. As pot plants for use in decorative work.

Bedding Displays

Bedding is a method of displaying plants in a colourful and collective way. Traditionally, bedding uses plants in a formal way, the plants being placed to create arrangements or patterns. In Victorian times, bedding was widely used; but because of the limited plant material then available, often the colour schemes were based only on red (*Pelargonium*), blue (*Lobelia*) and yellow (*Calceolaria*). While we still use these plants today, there is now a tremendous selection of plants from which to choose, bedding plants being available in a wide range of colours, habits and sizes.

The two main bedding displays are summer bedding and spring bedding. Other types of bedding of a more specialised nature can also be used, such as carpet bedding and plunge bedding.

Preparing and Planning a Site for Bedding

Bedding plants will grow in a number of soils, but ideally a loamy soil which is clay based gives best results. If your bed is to house summer bedding and spring bedding all year round, then you would simply cultivate your soil after each bed has been cleared before you plant the bed up with the next display. At this stage you may wish to work in a little organic matter or add a little fertiliser.

Before any planting is carried out, you should produce a plan or planting design of your bed.

Example: Bed 6 m × 3 m.

} Edging plant: usually a small plant, for example *Lobelia 'Cambridge Blue'*.

// Main groundwork plant: the size of this can vary depending on design, but a medium sized plant such as *Salvia 'Blaze of Fire'* can be used.

o Dot plant: this is used to break up the groundwork plant, so adding a little more interest to the design. Often such plants have coloured foliage and are slightly taller than the groundwork plant, an example being *Cineraria maritima*.

{} Standard: a plant or plants used to give the bed height. If one plant only is used, it is usually sited in the centre of the design. An example is standard *Fuchsia*.

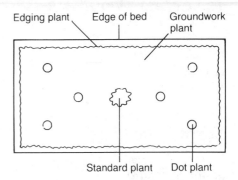

Using bedding plants

Planting

1. First plant your edging plants. Decide how far apart you want them and plant accordingly; you may wish to use a line to help keep your plants straight. Remember, plant at least 150 mm in from the edge of the bed, otherwise your plants may well grow over the edge and cause maintenance problems.
2. Next plant the standard plant(s) and dot plants.
3. Finally plant the groundwork plants – begin at one end of the bed and work across to the other end.

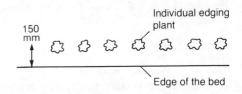

Planting edging plants

> **! ! REMEMBER**
>
> Decide on your planting distances for each group of plants. You should then be able to calculate the number of plants you will need.

Bed Maintenance

Immediately after planting, all plants should be watered in; this is particularly important with summer bedding plants if conditions are dry. Check that your standard plants remain tied securely throughout the season. Remove dead flower heads immediately, as the majority of bedding plants respond to this by producing more flower heads. Weed control is on-going throughout the season; in beds of this nature it is usually done either by hand weeding or hoeing or both. Also, in formal beds keep an eye out for plants which have not come true to type, as these will detract from your design. Such plants (know as rogues) should be removed.

The Colour Wheel

Primary colours	*Secondary colours*
1. Red	1. Purple
2. Blue	2. Orange
3. Yellow	3. Green

Types of Bedding

Summer Bedding

Half-hardy annuals are the main plants used for summer bedding. Beds are planted out at the end of May (depends on late frosts) and they are not lifted until the end of the summer.

Spring Bedding

A combination of plants can be used for this type of bedding. Particularly popular are biennial plants (plants that take two years to complete their life-cycle), such as *Myosotis* or Wallflowers, and bulbs such as Tulips.

Plunge Bedding

This is a type of successional bedding. A bed may have a number of schemes/designs over the year. Very often plants remain in their pots and are plunged into the bed (pots covered). This method maintains a high degree of interest year round, but is expensive to carry out.

Carpet Bedding

This uses small/dwarf species of plants (summer), which are slow growing, compact and have colourful foliage. Traditionally used in parks departments, the technique is in decline today as it is costly to carry out.

The colour wheel

! ! REMEMBER

When designing your bedding scheme, make sure you give enough thought to the colour scheme. All colours should make your arrangement pleasant and easy to look at.

 TIP

The colour wheel will help you to select colours that complement and harmonise with each other.

Bedding Plants – Examples

Name	Type*	Colour(s)	Height (mm)
Ageratum	HHA	Blue/mauve	100–150
Alyssum	HHA	White/pink	50–100
Lobelia	HHA	Blue/white	50–100
Petunia	HHA	Mixed	150–300
Pelargonium	TP	Mixed	200–300
Wallflowers	B	Mixed	200–300
Begonia	HHA	Mixed	100–300
Antirrhinum	HHA	Mixed	200–350
Calendula	HA	Orange/yellow	300–450
Nigella	HA	Blue	250
Godetia	HA	Pink	200–300
Clarkia	HA	Pink	200–300
Eschscholzia	HA	Orange	300–350
Cornflower	HA	Blue	300–600
Marigolds	HHA	Mixed	100–600
Myosotis	B	Blue	300
Limnanthus	HA	Yellow	100
Alternanthena	TP†	Foliage	50
Echeveria	TP†	Foliage	50
Heliotrope	TP	Purple	300
Verbena	HHA	Mixed	300
Salvia	HHA	Red	200–250
Amaranthus	HA	Red	300–400

* HA   = Hardy Annual.
  HHA = Half-Hardy Annual.
  B   = Biennial.
  TP   = Tender Perennial.
† Suitable for carpet bedding.

 TO DO

Design a summer bedding scheme for a bed of 5 m × 4 m. Use an example of each of the following plants: edging, groundwork, dot plant and standard plant. Consult the colour wheel and your tutor for guidance.

✱ **FOR INTEREST**

Some of the plants in the list are generally not classified as bedding plants, for example *Calendula*, *Nigella*, *Godetia* and *Clarkia*. However, these plants are being used more and more for the purpose of bedding.

Rock Gardens

Rock garden

Rock gardens can make excellent ornamental features; they are informal and if properly sited and constructed they should represent a natural outcrop. Rock gardens provide the right kind of environment for a range of plants and not just the true alpine plants. Here are just some examples that we can grow effectively in a rock garden:

1. True alpines
2. Sub-alpines
3. Dwarf shrubs
4. Dwarf conifers
5. Dwarf bulbs.

The rock garden can also feature pools and running water, and good use can be made of rock slopes. Visually the rock garden can be a very interesting ornamental feature all year round.

Choosing a Suitable Site

Ideally a gently sloping site would provide you with good development potential. You are trying to create a part of a mountain/hill side, a rocky outcrop, and in the most natural looking way you can. If your site has no natural slope to it but is suitable in other ways, it is possible to create your own slopes in one of two ways:

1. *Cut and fill* – dig out areas on your site and use the soil to make mounds or ridges.

2. *Import soil to site* – decide on how much soil you require and have it delivered to your site. Use the soil to create your own mounds. Check this soil for perennial weeds!

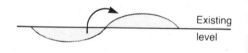

Cut and fill

Other factors to consider are:

(a) *Soil type* – your soil has to be freely drained. Plants associated with rock gardens need an open, well drained soil.
(b) *Shelter* – give your site some protection against wind.
(c) *An open aspect* – shade needs to be kept to a minimum, the garden needs good light.
(d) *Tree root invasions* – do not construct your garden too near mature trees; their roots may cause problems, not least of which is competition with your plants for food and water.
(e) *Water supply* – should you decide to incorporate a water feature in the garden, you will need a mains supply close at hand.

 TIP

Also avoid a site which has large deciduous trees. Leaf drop in autumn will smother the dwarf alpines.

Preparation and Construction

Preparation

Once you have decided on your site, you will need to cultivate it and remove all perennial weeds. These tasks can be carried out using mechanical methods and also herbicides. It is of great importance that you check your site for drainage; if necessary incorporate shale or rubble. You may have to consider a piped drainage scheme or a soak-away if your base soil is poor. During cultivations, work in suitable organic matter such as garden compost; applications of grit will also prove to be very useful at this stage.

 TIP

Should you wish to grow plants that require a more acid or alkaline pH, you can create pockets of soil throughout the garden as required. For very small or slow growing plants, place them in a suitably sized container and plant the container in the appropriate part of the garden.

 TO DO

Carry out a soil pH test; ideally the optimum pH of 6.5 ensures that you can grow successfully a wide range of plants in the garden.

Construction

Firstly decide on the rock type for the garden. The two most common types used are (a) limestone and (b) sandstone.

Once you have decided on the rock type, your garden will be known by that type. For example, if you chose limestone, you will have a limestone rock garden. If your preference is for acid-loving plants, then sandstones (non-limey) are ideal. If, however, you want to grow alkaline plants, limestones (non-acid) are preferable.

Where possible, use different sized rocks; this will give you the advantage of varying the height and visually will make the garden more interesting. For large pieces of rock you will need mechanical aids, winches and tractors. Numerous other implements may well be needed in moving and positioning rock.

✳ FOR INTEREST

Acid-loving plants are known as Calcifuges.
Alkaline-loving plants are known as Calcicoles.

Positioning the Rock

The rock garden should be built around the 'keystone', this is usually the biggest rock in the garden and it should be sited near to the bottom of the garden. All the other rock should then be positioned to match the strata and tilt of the keystone.

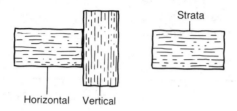

Wrongly matched strata

Correctly matched strata

Rock strata and placement

> **!! REMEMBER**
>
> When you position your rock you need to give it a tilt (backwards). Strata refers to the grain of the rock.

> ⚠ **SAFETY**
>
> When moving rock, care should be taken and safe lifting procedures carried out.

> **TIP**
>
> When positioning rock, choose the most weathered pieces for the top and outer edges of your garden. Once again, this makes the rock look more natural.

A backward tilt or slope is given to the rock not only to give it a more natural appearance but also because the rock will find it much easier to shed rainfall. When positioning rock, you should aim to cover at least half of it; this also helps to give the impression of a natural outcrop.

Planting the Rock Garden

As the majority of plants suitable for the rock garden are grown in containers, planting can be done at any time of the year depending on existing weather conditions. However, autumn is considered a good time for planting as this should give the plants a little time to get established before being subjected to winter conditions. Plants should be put in at the same depth as they were in their containers. Remove each plant from its container, plant it firmly and water in.

Care should be taken at planting time; you do not want to plant in the wrong conditions/aspect. For example, those alpines with grey downy type leaves/stems can become damaged by high rainfall. Such plants should not be positioned at the base of backward tilting rocks as rainfall will shed off the rocks onto the plants.

> ✳ **FOR INTEREST**
>
> Covering half the rock with soil helps produce a cool root run for the plants. It also helps to support the rocks.

Maintaining Rock Gardens

Conventional rock gardens will need a great deal of maintenance. Weeding usually has the highest priority, and on old and well established rock gardens this operation is done by hand. The use of herbicides should be restricted as damage to plants becomes a real danger. Ideally weeds, particularly perennial weeds, are best identified early at seedling stage; this will make their control much easier. However, this is often not as easy as it sounds as many of the alpines shed seed and it can be difficult to tell the difference between weed and plant seedlings. Herbicides are usually used as a spot treatment on established rock gardens. Here the herbicide is applied to the surface of a weed plant, and if it is a systemic herbicide it will be moved throughout the plant and should give a total kill.

Another regular maintenance operation involves the clipping off of dead flower/seed heads after flowering. This is important because otherwise your garden could be overrun with unwanted seedlings.

Weed-free Rock Gardens

It is possible to construct a rock garden in conjunction with a polythene mulch. Black heavy-duty polythene is used to cover the soil between the rock pieces. The plants are put in through the polythene; after planting, the whole area is covered with chippings. The chippings must match the rock pieces; for example, if you have used limestone rock you will need to use limestone chippings. The chippings should completely cover the polythene. Your plants can grow quite successfully through it and if done correctly, this gives excellent weed control.

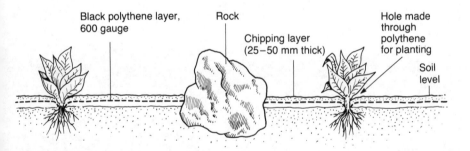

Using a polythene mulch

Alternative Methods of Growing Alpines

Alpines, and other plants we normally associate with rock gardens, can be grown in other ways:

1. Retaining walls: suitable for trailing plants.
2. Paved areas: spaces left in patios can be planted with alpines.
3. Raised beds: a formal way of presenting and growing alpines.
4. Sinks and troughs: very useful for growing tiny alpines.
5. Alpine house: specific glasshouses for the growing of alpines.
6. Screes: the use of small rock pieces/chippings as a bed in its own right. Screes are very often used in conjunction with rock gardens as they complement each other so well.
7. Alpine meadows: if your site is large enough you can surround the garden with un-cut grassed areas, a type of meadow. This area can be planted with taller alpine species and alpine bulbous plants. This is very effective in the spring and early summer.
8. Peat gardens: used for growing acid-loving alpines. Peat blocks are used to construct a variety of bed shapes and sizes.
9. Hypertufa pots: man-made material using grit sand, peat, cement and water. It is possible to make or mould rock shapes with planting holes. It is often used to cover a glazed sink, producing a stone-like appearance.

Examples of Rock Garden Plants

Dwarf conifers
Abies balsamea 'Hudsonia'
Chamaecyparis lawsoniana 'Ellwoods Gold'
Chamaecyparis lawsoniana 'Minima Aurea'
Chamaecyparis lawsoniana 'Minima Glauca'
Chamaecyparis obtusa 'Nana Gracilis'
Juniperus squamata 'Blue Star'
Picea abies 'Nidiformis'
Picea glauca albertiana 'Conica'
Thuja orientalis 'Aurea Nana'

Dwarf shrubs
Berberis darwinii 'Nana'
Daphne cneorum
Erica x darleyensis
Genista villarsii
Rhododendron glaucophyllum
Hebe pinguifolia 'Pagei'

Alpines (for a sunny open site)
Achillea tomentosa
Aethionema 'Warley Rose'
Dianthus species
Erinus alpinus
Helianthemum species
Penstemon Fruticosus
Phlox douglasii
Sedum spurium

Alpines (for a shady site)
Epimedium alpinum
Mimulus luteus 'Guttatus'
Oxalis species
Primula species (if moisture is present)

Bulbs
Anemone blanda
Crocus species
Cyclamen neapolitanum
Galanthus nivalis
Iris reticulata
Narcissus bulbocodium
Tulipa tarda

Alpines (for walls)
Aubrieta deltoides
Dianthus deltoides
Iberis semperflorens
Phlox subulata
Cerastium tomentosa

Alpines (for acid beds or gardens)
Gentiana species
Lewisia species
Lithospermum diffusum
Pulsatilla species

> ✳ **FOR INTEREST**
>
> The Saxifraga group of alpines is an important group of alpines. They are often used, according to species, in a variety of rock gardening sites and situations.

Containers

Containers are now used extensively in Amenity Horticulture; they have great versatility, which means they can be used in a wide variety of sites and situations. Where garden areas are small, containers can be used successfully to grow a wide range of outdoor plants. Traditionally clay pots were used, but today a wide variety of containers made from various materials can be used.

Here are just some of the containers available today:

1. Clay pots – various shapes and sizes.
2. Wooden containers – full barrels, half barrels, squares and rectangles.
3. Plastic containers – various shapes, sizes and colours.
4. Concrete containers – various shapes, sizes and colours.
5. Window boxes – made from numerous materials.
6. Hanging baskets – plastic or traditional wire baskets.
7. Troughs – usually made from stone or concrete.
8. Urns – made from a range of materials.
9. Chimney pots – various sizes and designs.

Choosing a Container

When choosing a container, you will have to give the matter a good deal of thought. Although you may not have realised it, there are a number of factors that limit your choice.

The following points should be considered:

1. Weight – decide where you want to put your container. Is it for a permanent site or do you wish to move it around? Remember, containers come in all types of materials, and this is an important consideration.
2. Size – take into account the overall size of height and width you require.
3. Durability – how long will your container last? Will it be able to withstand long periods of cold weather?
4. Depth – containers will vary in the depth they give. If your plant is hardy and you wish to grow it permanently in a container, make sure the container is deep enough. You will need to know the vigour of your plant and to check whether it will be suited to a containerised life.
5. Drainage – every container, irrespective of type of construction material, will need drainage holes. Drainage is of great importance to containerised plants.

Planting Containers

Once you have decided on your plants, you will need to consider suitable growing media/composts. If your plants are to be permanently in containers, a compost based on a John Innes mix is generally of greater value than one based on peat-based composts. However, for acid-loving plants, a peat-based compost is ideal. Containers that are used solely for alternate spring and summer bedding plants are generally filled with peat-based compost (loamless).

 TO DO

Make a list of plants suitable for containers, both long term and short term. For each plant, decide on the best growing medium for it.

 REMEMBER

All plants grown in containers, whether they be long term or short term, will benefit from feeding. Containerised plants can be fed by foliar feeds, or by adding slow release fertiliser granules to the compost.

Maintenance of Containers

Container gardening requires little all-year-round maintenance, but it really does depend on the season. Containers used solely for summer bedding plants will need constant attention, daily even, if the days are hot and dry. Watering containers in summer is an essential part of their maintenance as they can dry out quickly, particularly if they are sited in full sun. Pruning of the permanent plants will be needed from time to time, and dead heading of all flowering plants is required to maintain the containers' appearance. In winter, check to see if your containers have been frost damaged and that they are still in good order. Wooden containers will need to be preserved, by frequent painting or application of wood treatments, to keep them in good condition.

 SAFETY

Even small containers can be heavy. Make sure you exercise safe lifting techniques when moving containers.

Positioning Containers

If your container is reasonably hard wearing, you only need to consider its size when you site it. Small patios should not be used for large containers, and vice versa; the balance would not be right. Window boxes and hanging baskets need to be firmly secured. On large patios, containers of different sizes but of the same type, such as mixed sized clay pots, can look very effective if positioned carefully.

Containers can look effective on the tops of low walls, but remember they are then more vulnerable to being knocked over.

TIP

Use building bricks to give height to containers. This is a particularly useful idea if you intend to group the containers. If done correctly, you should lose sight of the bricks in due course.

⚠ **SAFETY**

With all containers, make sure they are positioned in a safe and unobstructive manner. Hanging baskets, for example, should ideally be positioned above head height.

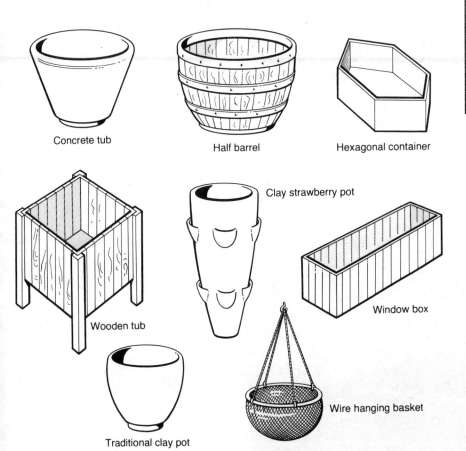

Concrete tub

Half barrel

Hexagonal container

Wooden tub

Clay strawberry pot

Window box

Traditional clay pot

Wire hanging basket

Container types

3 RECREATIONAL HORTICULTURE

Turfculture

Turfculture is the cultivation of grass. In Amenity Horticulture, grass has many uses ranging from ornamental lawns to sports pitches. Grass is essentially a form of permanent ground cover and can, when established, be transplanted indefinitely. Grass is a very important plant although most people take it for granted. As an amenity feature it tends to dominate our parks and gardens, and a whole host of recreational activities require it. The understanding and cultivation of grass (turfculture) is of fundamental importance to amenity horiticulturists, whose work brings them into daily contact with it. People who work with turf become specialists and are known as groundstaff.

Playing field

The individual grass species that make up turf depend on what the turf is to be used for. If you want to establish an ornamental lawn, the fine grass species can be used. However, should the requirement be for a winter sportsfield, the coarser species would be used. We can also mix fine and coarse species to produce a turf to fit whatever amenity area we require. In this way it is possible to produce the right surface for ornamental areas – sportsfields, motorway verges and many more. As you can see, the range of turf types is large; because of this, management of turf areas involves a great deal more than just mowing. Managers of turf areas and groundstaff who are involved with recreational turf are aware that sports pitches and parks are now being used more intensively than they once were. One of the reasons for this is that most people today have increased leisure time. Much of this leisure time is spent in or on amenity facilities, both in the private and public sectors.

Growing Turf

Lawns or recreational playing surfaces can be established in one of two ways:

(1) from seed
(2) from turf.

Both methods are acceptable and can effectively produce the desired result. However, there are a number of points to consider:

1. *How quickly do you need your surface?* Turfing will provide you with an immediate surface and would be ready for use as a playing surface in a much shorter time than seed.
2. *What preparations are involved?* Seeding will require longer and more detailed preparation compared with the preparations for turfing.
3. *What are the costs?* Per square metre seeding will be much cheaper than turf, even allowing for extra preparations.
4. *Which will produce the better surface?* In the short term, turf if correctly managed should produce a good surface, but it does depend on the type and quality of the turf used. After a period of establishment and correct management, seeding will produce a good surface. It will certainly be comparable with, if not better than, turf.

Preparing the Site

If the site is level, cultivations can begin. If the site is uneven for some reason, grading will be required. This is done by moving soil on the site to make it more level; if appropriate, top soil can be brought to the site to help in this procedure. On a large scale, cultivations are carried out using various mechanical implements ranging from rotavators to tractor-drawn ploughs. On a small scale, digging can be just as effective. When using mechanical equipment for cultivations, beware of compaction/panning problems. Such problems are often associated with clay soils when cultivated in wet weather. Once the initial cultivations have been carried out, seedbed preparations can begin. This involves the breaking down of large clods. This can be done on a small scale using the back of a garden fork and rake; for large operations, use tractor-mounted harrows.

X   USEFUL TERMS

Grading   The removal of top soil and subsoil.

TIP

Subsoiling could be carried out after draining and before top soil cultivations begin. This will help reduce compaction problems later.

Drainage

Drainage is a very important practical consideration when trying to grow and establish grass. For the successful establishment of the majority of cultivated grass species, the soil needs to be well drained. If soil remains wet for prolonged periods it can become physically damaged, for example it can lose both its structure and texture. Grass species suitable for ornamental lawns and sportsfields are easily damaged by water-logged conditions – yellowing, stunting and die-back are all symptoms of poorly drained turf. In general terms, where growing conditions are poor, you can expect root growth and development to be poor also. Winter sports pitches often become water-logged in winter through a combination of intensive use, high rainfall and poor maintenance.

⚠ **SAFETY**

If the top of a playing surface has frozen during winter, playing conditions can become hazardous or in many cases impossible.

Drainage Systems

The ideal time to consider and then, if necessary, install a drainage system is at the preparation stage. The natural drainage of a site can be improved by adding suitable materials, such as grit sand, to the soil. This will improve natural drainage and is a helpful drainage aid on clay sites. The material can be worked into the soil prior to seedbed preparations.

If it is considered that the site would also benefit from a piped system, which is often the case when dealing with recreational areas, one of the following two systems can be used:

(1) Herringbone system
(2) Grid system.

On sportsfields where the field or pitch is surrounded by other land which may or may not have been drained, run-off water will be a problem. Run-off water is water that will encroach onto the playing surface and may over-load the piped system. To avoid this, a series of 'cut-off drains' can be put in on the boundary edges.

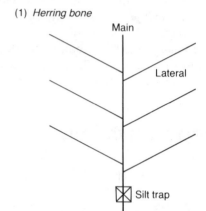

(1) *Herring bone*

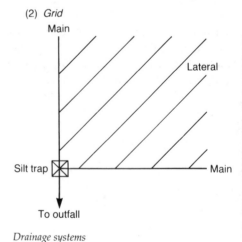

(2) *Grid*

Drainage systems

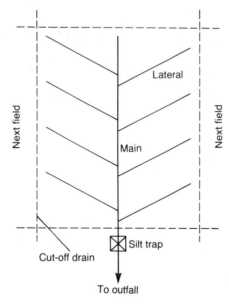

Installation of cut-off drain on a piped drainage system

!! **REMEMBER**

Piped systems have to be laid on gradients for water flow. Gradients of 1/100 to 1/200 are usually used.

Drainage Problems

The main problems surrounding drainage are concerned with the natural ability of a soil to drain. However, these problems can be aggravated by man in a number of ways.

The following list represents the different ways in which drainage can be impeded:

1. *Natural high water table*: will impede water movement.
2. *Slow permeability*: if the soil is unable to drain quickly, this often indicates a problem with both soil texture and soil structure. Undetected, this can quickly lead to a water-logged top soil.
3. *Perched water table*: this can be created naturally in poor soil or artificially by man. Cultivations using pedestrian-operated cultivators or tractor-drawn ploughs can, under certain circumstances, cause a smearing of the soil. This leads to the formation of a pan which, if left undisturbed, will become impervious to water. If this happens in top soil or subsoil, the water table is said to be 'perched'.
4. *Springs*: if natural springs are present on or near the site they will cause problems for drainage. Here the area would be moist or wet all year round, and therefore liable to waterlogging.

 USEFUL TERMS

Water table Water collected naturally or artifically sitting at a certain height in the soil.
Permeability The openess/drainage capacity of a soil.

Identifying Impeded Drainage on Turf

1. *Surface water*: this is the main symptom of impeded drainage. If surface water is left, it will destroy soil texture and soil structure and almost certainly lead to die-back.
2. *Patchiness*: patches of turf will show die-back symptoms, such as yellowing, stunting and loss of vigour.
3. *Indicator weeds*: a number of weeds can help you identify impeded or poor drainage on turf. The following list of drainage indicator weeds provides some examples:

    (a) Self Heal (in quantity)
    (b) Creeping Buttercup (in quantity)
    (c) Feathery Moss
    (d) Horsetail
    (e) Coltsfoot

4. *Soil discolouration*: blue, grey or orange colours found in the subsoil suggest poor drainage and growing conditions for turf.
5. *Peaty formations*: on poorly drained turf, a layer of peat is often found just below grass leaf level – it brings a spongy-like characteristic to the turf.

Weed Control

Weed control is an important practical consideration in the establishment of a lawn or playing fields. Perennial weeds ideally should be eradicated during your site preparations; otherwise it will be difficult to achieve a good establishment.

‼ **REMEMBER**

Perennial weeds may not just be broadleaved weeds. Many perennial weeds are grasses, or weed grasses as they are often called. If such grasses are allowed to grow with cultivated species, it will be at the expense of the species.

 FOR INTEREST

Fallowing could also be used as a method of weed control.

Provided you have enough time prior to site cultivations, the site can be sprayed using suitable translocated (systemic) herbicides. Such chemicals are absorbed on contact with the weed, and move around the plant's system from leaf to root; this means the whole plant is contaminated. More than one application may be required for the chemical to be effective, but in due course a good control should be achieved.

Annual weeds can also be controlled in a similar way to that used for perennial weeds.

Fertilisers

Whether your grass is to be grown from seed or turf, it will benefit from an application of suitable fertilisers which can be incorporated into the soil before sowing or laying turf. In either case the most important nutrient required is phosphate. This nutrient is vital to the growth and development of a good root system; it is usually applied as Superphosphate (18% soluble P_2O_5) at a rate of 40–50 g/m^2.

However, for all round seedling development or turf establishment, a dressing of suitable nitrogenous and potassic fertilisers should also be given.

▶▶▶ **TO DO**

Make a list of herbicides that can be used to clear a site of weeds before site cultivations begin.

 SAFETY

Dealing with chemicals is potentially dangerous. Be trained in their application or seek advice from a specialist.

Site Preparation Checklist

1. Remove all perennial and annual weeds prior to site cultivations. This work should be done well in advance of sowing seed or laying turf; 6–9 months before would be ideal. Also, remove any surface debris from the site.
2. *Site levelling*. The site should be graded or levelled as necessary and consolidated as appropriate. Ideally, the soil for seed sowing or turf should have a minimum top soil depth of 150 mm, otherwise root development may be restricted.
3. *Soil testing*. Make a pH survey of the site. A slightly acid soil will help the development of your cultivated species, particularly if fine leaved species are used. A slightly acid soil will also help in the control of a number of weeds.
4. Decide whether a drainage system is needed. Install the system early in the site preparations.
5. *Primary site cultivations*. Use suitable tools and equipment according to the size of the site. Take care not to produce any pans.
6. *Secondary site cultivations/seed bed preparations*. Produce the final tilth before seed sowing or turfing; select and use appropriate tools and equipment. The final tilth for seeding should be finer than that used for turfing. Finally level and consolidate.
7. Before seed sowing or turfing, apply suitable fertilisers, particularly those of the major plant nutrients – N, P, K (nitrogen, phosphorus, potassium). Such fertilisers will aid the establishment of the seed or turf.
8. *Seeding*. If seed has been used, on germination an application of a suitable seedling selective herbicide will prevent weed seedlings from competing with your young grass seedlings.

 TIP

To check out impeded drainage, dig a series of test holes, 900 mm × 900 mm × 900 mm. The resulting soil profile should show you if there are any defects concerning drainage.

Establishing a Lawn from Seed

Seed Sowing

The time to sow grass seed is either in the spring or in early autumn; at these times, conditions for germination should be just about right. Grass seed is no different from other seed when it comes to germination – warmth, air, moisture and a well prepared seed bed are all basic requirements for success. However, it is possible to sow grass seed throughout the year if the ideal times cannot be met. Remember, if sowing in the summer irrigation may well be required during drought conditions. Grass seed will germinate in adverse or poor weather conditions, for example, during the winter, but establishment will be slow and patchy.

How to Sow

There are many ways in which grass seed can be sown. On a small garden scale it is often done by hand – broadcasting the seed as you walk over the site. The easiest way of sowing by hand is to divide up the site into 1 m squares using pegs and lines, and sow each square individually.

On larger areas, for example playing fields, the seed is often drilled. This is done by using specialist tractor-mounted machinery which takes out channels in the soil and drills the seed accordingly. An example of such an implement is a contravator; this drills seed in straight lines, which means that on germination the grass comes up in straight lines. However, as the grass grows and develops, the lines grow into each other and in a short time no lines can be seen. The alternative method is to broadcast sow using tractor-mounted spreaders.

! ! REMEMBER

Ideal sowing times are:
1. Late March to early May
2. Late August to late September.

  TIP

Make sure your seed has been treated with a bird repellent. This will help reduce the seed loss.

Sowing Rates

How much you sow per square metre depends on the surface you are trying to produce. For lawns I would recommend a sowing rate of about 35 g/m^2; under normal circumstances this should produce a reasonably good grass cover. On larger areas this rate could be increased by half as much again or even doubled if it was thought that birds, rodents or other germination restrictions were going to be a problem.

On a garden scale, it may help to make a plan for sowing. For example:

1. Work out the amount of seed you need for the site:
   area of site (m^2) × sowing rate (per m^2).
2. Mark out in square metres the whole of the site.
3. Measure/weigh out enough seed for 1 m^2.
4. Sow each square metre accordingly.
5. After sowing, gently rake in your seed; try and cover as much of the seed as possible.

Seed and Seedling Diseases

There are several diseases which attack both the seed and the young seedling plants; they are known as 'damping-off diseases'. These diseases are divided into two groups:

1. *Pre-emergence damping off.* This disease attacks the seed and if it is successful will stop it from germinating. To help reduce its attack, make sure the seed has been treated with a suitable fungicide. Bare patches on your site at germination time may indicate the presence of this disease.
2. *Post-emergence damping off.* This disease affects the seedling stage and so occurs after germination. Symptoms of attack are yellowing and wilting of individual seedlings, resulting in its eventual death. Once again, seed dressings of suitable fungicides can help prevent this problem.

 TIP

Damping-off diseases can be reduced by not sowing in cool/cold conditions. Also, use a good quality seed (treated) in conjunction with a pre-seeding fertiliser, and sow at low rates.

Growing a Lawn from Turf

Growing a lawn from turf is a much quicker method compared with seed – you will, in effect, produce an instant lawn. The commercial production of turf today allows us to select the type and quality of turf we require, so that it is possible to establish a wide range of surfaces from bowling greens to winter sports' pitches. As you would expect, establishing a surface from turf is more expensive than seeding, but you gain the required surface in the shortest possible time.

On the turf nursery, turves are cut to various sizes and, should it be required, even rolled up in strips of different lengths.

Lifting and Storing Turf

On a commercial scale, turf is lifted using specialist turf-cutting and lifting equipment. The equipment uses a series of knife-like blades, one vertical and the other horizontal, and is set to cut at appropriate depths and thicknesses. On a smaller scale, turves can be lifted using a hand-held turf-lifting iron as shown in the adjoining diagram.

The correct thickness of the turf is important. If you cut the turves too thinly, you may lose much of their root system; if they are cut too thick, once laid they will take some time to root through to the soil surface.

Once lifted, turves can be boxed-off and trimmed with a turf-knife to produce the required thickness. Individual turves, after being lifted, should ideally only be stored for 3–4 days. Turves are often stored in stacks, and as such are vulnerable to drying winds; if high winds are experienced, the stacks should be covered. If turf has to be stored for long periods, it should not be stacked but laid out on moist ground, keeping the turves tightly packed.

Turf Quality

When ordering or looking for turf, you should check out its quality. Many different types of turf are offered today, for particular uses, but sadly standards do vary. In general, turf should be:

1. Of an even size, for example 300 mm × 300 mm or 300 mm × 450 mm.
2. Each slab of turf should have the same thickness; this is an important practical consideration to make laying of the turf easier.
3. Ideally, the turf should be weed free; this is often not the case for low quality turf.
4. The turf should have a good blend of grass species which should meet your specified requirements.

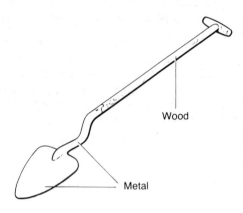

Wood

Metal

Turf-lifting iron

TIP

When stacking turves, you should stack them soil to soil and grass to grass.

Laying Turf

Provided you have prepared a suitable and level seed bed, the laying of turf is a straightforward task. Here are some practical guidelines to follow:

1. Begin at one end of the site.
2. Lay your turves as if you were laying bricks; in this way your turves will become bonded.

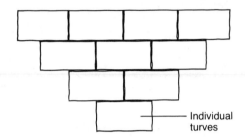

Bonding is essential when laying turf

3. Work over your laid turves and do not stand on your prepared seed bed. Use a suitable plank or board to work off, placing it on top of the turves and moving it as necessary.
4. Have a bucket of fine soil or compost mix with you when turfing. You may need handfuls of soil for packing purposes should your seed bed crumble.
5. Once all the turf has been laid, finish off by spreading a suitable soil or compost mix over the whole of the site and work this into your turf. This can be done by using either a stiff brush or a trulute (see page 60). This will assist rooting and help prevent excessive drying out.

 TIP

Make sure you lay whole turves at the edges of your site. This is much better than using small pieces of turf as edge fillers, because the turf can establish itself more easily.

! ! REMEMBER

Turf-laying can be carried out all year round, but only if weather conditions are suitable.

Turf Maintenance

After Seeding

Once good germination has been achieved, both the site and the seedlings will benefit from a light rolling. This will help to firm up the soil around the seedlings and promote tillering (horizontal shoot production). The first cut should take the form of a light trim; aim to cut no lower than 25–30 mm, you do not want to take off too much leaf at this stage – you are trying to encourage more vigorous growth. As the grass continues to grow and develop you can steadily reduce the height of cut to its required finish, and also decide upon a cutting frequency, such as weekly, fortnightly and so on.

After Turfing

Check that no gaps appear between the turves; if they do you will need to apply a suitable top dressing. In warm conditions and without irrigation, turves may shrink; therefore make sure you irrigate as appropriate. Once you feel the turves have begun to establish themselves, you can give your site its first cut and from then on adopt a similar programme as for seed.

Maintaining Established Lawns

Whether you have established your lawn from seed or turf, you will at some point need to draw up and adopt a programme of planned maintenance. Such a programme is of vital importance if you are to grow and present a quality grass surface.

Maintaining turf involves many individual tasks, various tools and mechanical equipment, but above all you must have a good knowledge of grounds maintenance; training in turfculture therefore has a key role to play. The following tasks are associated with turf maintenance:

1. Mowing
2. Edging
3. Feeding
4. Rolling
5. Watering
6. Aeration
7. Brushing and scarifying
8. Top dressing
9. Repairs
10. Weed control
11. Pest and disease control

Mowing: Regular mowing will help produce a dense sward, but beware of cutting too keenly as the turf could be damaged. Cutting can be continued throughout the winter months provided conditions are favourable. Selection of mower is important – on fine turf, cylinder mowers should be used; on coarse turf, rotary mowers are preferable. The turf machinery industry has provided us with a very wide selection of machines from which to choose; make sure you choose the right machine for the job.

Edging: Select appropriate tools, for example a half-moon, a line, a board and either a turf-lifting iron or a spade. The edges of lawns are kept straight and tidy using a line, half-moon and, if necessary, a board which you should use to work off. Once the edges have been trimmed, the trimmings can be lifted using the turf-lifting iron or a spade, and removed from site.

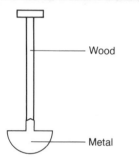

— Wood

— Metal

Half-moon edging iron

Feeding: To help keep turf looking good, regular feeding is required. If feeding is carried out correctly, it should help promote the fine grass species but discourage the weeds and weed grasses. From spring to mid summer apply ammonium sulphate (21% N) at approximately 20g/m². An autumn dressing of a suitable phosphorus and potassium fertiliser, for example Superphosphate and potassium sulphate at a ratio of 2:1 applied at approximately 70g/m², can also be given.

▶ ▶ ▶ TO DO

Make a list of the different types of cylinder and rotary grass-cutting machinery available.

! ! REMEMBER

Your choice of mower should reflect the standard of maintenance you require.

 TIP

If the machine has an oil sump, the mower has a 4-stroke engine. If no oil sump is present, the mower has a 2-stroke engine.

▶ ▶ ▶ TO DO

Make a list of the *pre-start checks* you would carry out before actually using your mowing machine.

A cylinder mower and a rotary mower

! ! REMEMBER

If ammonium sulphate is applied under certain conditions or not watered in, it could scorch the grass.

Rolling: Some rolling of the surface may be needed during the season. It should be done when the surface is moist but not wet, and on ornamental lawns light rollers only should be used. Rolling will help consolidate the roots of newly sown grass, and in spring it is useful in helping to replace any turf which may have been lifted as a result of frost action.

Watering: Watering is often needed to aid the establishment of both newly sown grass and newly laid turf. Watering will also be required on established turf during drought conditions. Sprinklers are the best way of watering lawns; make sure the area is throroughly soaked at each watering.

Aeration: 1. *Surface aeration* – this is easily carried out on lawns by pricking the top 25 mm of the surface using either a garden fork or a studded roller. This task should be carried out throughout the summer.

2. *Sub-surface aeration* – this work is generally carried out from early autumn through to spring. This form of aeration is important to turf as it will help relieve compaction. Compaction on grass surfaces is a major concern to the groundstaff, and is a particular problem on winter sports pitches. Practically, sub-surface aeration is carried out using a variety of tools and equipment. The following equipment is available for use by hand or it can be tractor mounted; in this way both small and large areas can be dealt with.

(a) *Hollow tine*: this is pushed into and then pulled out of the turf; it brings with it a core of soil.

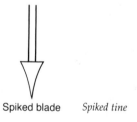

Core of soil released from the tine   *Hollow tine*

(b) *Spiked tine*: pushed into the turf it makes its hole as it displaces the soil.

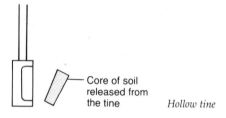

Spiked blade   *Spiked tine*

(c) *Slit tine*: pushed into the turf it makes a fine hole. It can also help to root prune turf.

Slit tine

TIP

On small ornamental lawns, the roller on your mowing machine may be just as effective as a purpose-built roller.

Brushing and scarifying: Brushing will remove some of the dead material in lawns and on fine turf, such as bowling greens, it will remove worm casts.

The scarification of turf is done using rakes; specialist rakes are available for either hand-held or tractor-mounted use. By scarifying turf you will remove any unwanted material from the surface, and it should raise tillers which can then be cut by the mower. Brushing is a continuous maintenance task. Although scarifying can be carried out frequently, it is mostly done in the spring and autumn.

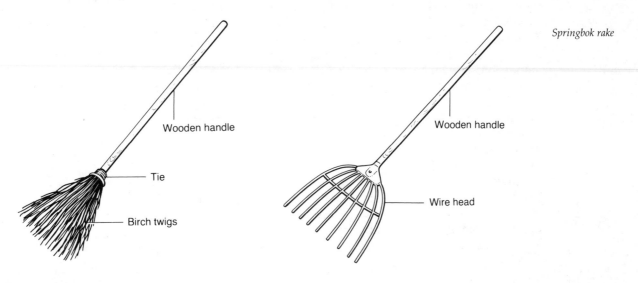

Springbok rake

Wooden handle

Wooden handle

Tie

Wire head

Birch twigs

Besom brush

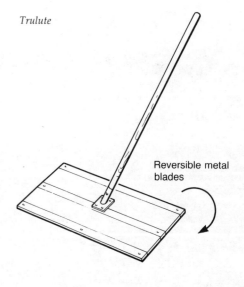

Trulute

Reversible metal blades

Top dressing: This is a material or a combination of materials based on loam or compost which is scattered over turf as a means of levelling the turf surface. The material, which is often applied in bulk form, will also help to increase the organic matter content of the turf and retain moisture in drought conditions; it will also encourage tillering. A mixture of sand, peat and loam with a little fertiliser applied in the autumn, at a rate of approximately 2.75 kg/m^2, is an ideal top dressing. This should be worked into the turf using either a trulute or a stiff brush.

Turf repairs: From time to time, bare patches will be produced; the easiest and quickest way to repair these is to re-turf them. Dig out the bare patch and cover it with a turf that has been cut and trimmed to fit exactly into position. However, often there is a problem in obtaining replacement turf similar to the existing turf. For this reason, Local Authority Parks Departments and large private gardens have turf nurseries. As an alternative to turfing, seeding can be carried out on bare patches. Fork over and prepare the patch, and re-seed with a similar seed mixture as your existing turf. September is an ideal time to do this.

Weed control: Keeping lawns or playing fields free from weeds is a difficult maintenance task. Weed control on amenity turf is both expensive and labour intensive. Decide on the standard you require for your turf; for example a bowling green (fine turf) could easily be destroyed by weeds, whereas a winter sports pitch (coarser turf) is able to withstand some weed invasion. Weeds in turf can be very damaging; they will compete for light, water and nutrients at the expense of the turf. Many of the weeds found growing in turf have become adapted in their growth pattern. Turf weeds will grow horizontally and not vertically, and can carry on their life cycle (including flowering and seeding) beneath the height of the bottom blade of a mower. The damaging turf weeds are characterised by having a tap root system or a series of creeping stems; dandelions and creeping buttercups are examples.

The presence of moss or pearlwort on turf tells you that your soil is in poor condition or that you are mowing your turf too closely. Moss will invade turf when poor drainage or heavy shade exists. To kill moss, use proprietary moss killers, however, it will come back if you do not avoid poor drainage, poor soil and shade.

Annual weeds are not a major problem on turf as very often they are mown out quite easily. For the tap-rooted perennial weeds you will need to use selective herbicides. These herbicides are specially formulated for use on turf; they will not damage the turf provided manufacturers' instructions are followed.

 SAFETY

When applying herbicides, follow manufacturers' instructions and wear the appropriate protective clothing.

 TIP

On a small lawn, use a hand-weeding tool or skewer and dig out tap rooted weeds by hand. This will give you immediate results.

 TO DO

Make a list of turf weeds and their controlling selective herbicides

Pest and Disease Control

Both pest and disease can cause considerable damage on turf. To control them effectively they need to be recognised early and control measures given as necessary. To do this, you will need to know and recognise the symptoms of damage from individual pests and diseases. To help with this, some of the main pests and diseases found on turf and their symptoms will be listed.

X   USEFUL TERM

Soil drench   This wets the soil without creating puddles.

Pests

1. *Leatherjackets*: These are the larvae of cranefly. They are between 25 and 35 mm long and a grey brown colour. They feed on grass roots. Symptoms to look for are a yellow discolouration of the grass and a general decline in growth. Where leatherjackets feed close to the surface they attract birds, particularly starlings.

    Leatherjackets are active feeders from early spring through to early summer.

    Control: use a suitable insecticide, for example, HCH applied as a soil drench.

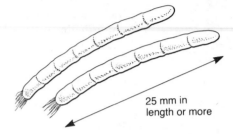

Leatherjackets (Cranefly larvae) can be a serious turf pest

2. *Wireworms*: These are the larvae of click beetles. They are about 25 mm long, when fully grown, and have a shiny orange coloured appearance. They are very slow moving and can be present in the soil for some time, as their life cycle is between 4 and 5 years. They feed on grass roots and when present in large populations can cause a great deal of damage. Patches of the lawn or turf will yellow and die-back, and growth and development will become impeded. Wireworms feed particularly heavily during spring and summer.

    Control: use a suitable insecticide – once again HCH can be used as soil drench.

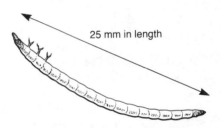

Wireworms (Click beetle larvae) can be a serious turf pest

3. *Swift moths*: The caterpillar (larval stage) of the swift moth causes damage to turf. Caterpillars vary in size, depending on the species of moth concerned; the garden swift moth caterpillar is about 30–35 mm in size and has a white/creamy body and a shiny brown head. The caterpillars feed throughout winter, with heavy feeding in early spring.

    Control: HCH or other suitable insecticide.

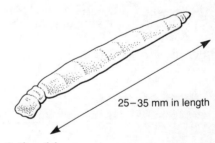

Swift moth larvae

Earthworms and moles can also cause problems on turf.

Diseases

1. *Fusarium patch disease*: This is one of the most common diseases of turf. It can be seen throughout the year. The disease is often found on poorly aerated turf and on turf which has had an over dressing of nitrogen.

    Symptoms to look for are small discoloured patches of turf, often yellow which quickly turns to brown. The patches often merge together to form large patches of yellowing turf.

    Control: suitable systemic fungicides, for example benomyl, will give some control.

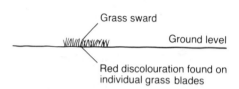

Dying turf—turning yellow/brown, which eventually turns white

Turf yet unaffected

Fusarium patch disease

2. *Red thread*: This is a disease that can be difficult to detect. Symptoms include a pinkish appearance on patches of turf. To confirm the presence of red thread, you will need to examine individual grass blades, which will contain reddish fungal growths.

    Red thread generally indicates poor drainage and a soil which is low in nitrogen. A combination of aeration and suitable nitrogen dressings will help reduce the frequency of this disease.

    Control: use suitable systemic fungicides.

Grass sward

Ground level

Red discolouration found on individual grass blades

Red thread disease

3. *Fairy rings*: Fairy rings are a frequent problem on turf – they appear as circles or patches of dead turf, of various sizes. Often these rings will merge together as the fungus responsible for them continues to grow. This can lead to very large circular areas of discoloured grass.

    Control: this is difficult, even for the specialist. Chemicals are used professionally, but on a small scale it is possible to dig out the rings and sterilise the hole with a domestic sterilant, and then introduce fresh clean healthy soil. After this, re-seed or re-turf as necessary. However, even this often has only limited success. There are many types of fairy rings, each with their own symptoms and characteristics, but all will show this ringing appearance.

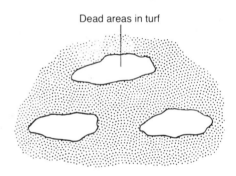

Dead areas in turf

Fairy rings

Other diseases of turf include: Damping-off
Dollar spot
Take all (formerly ophiolobus patch)
Rusts
Leaf spots
Virus

▶ ▶ ▶ **TO DO**

Make an examination of different turf areas. How many diseases can you find?

TIP

Systemic fungicides work best during the growing season, while contact sprays can be used all year round but are essential in winter.

Some Terms Used in Turf Maintenance

Aeration: the opening of the turf or soil, allowing air to circulate around the root system. It also makes drainage easier and water more available to the roots. Aeration is carried out by pedestrian-operated tools and equipment or by tractor-mounted equipment.

Compaction: this is the result of turf or soil being continually walked or played upon. It destroys soil structure and will make the movement of air and water impossible. Grass will make poor growth in compacted soil. Compaction is relieved through aeration.

Divot: a piece of turf kicked up by players on sportsturf. It is the groundstaff's job to replace these divots at the end of the game, or the players' responsibility in the case of golf.

Lute: a levelling tool, often used to work in top dressings.

Mat: dead grass which tends to remain near to the surface and so takes a long time to decay. If a mat is left on turf, it will affect aeration and water penetration. Regular scarification will remove a mat. It is also known as *thatch*.

Top dressing: a material applied to the surface and worked in with a brush or a lute. Its main function is to level the surface.

Rolling: the use of a roller to help consolidate the turf surface.

Scarifying: the removal of dead grass at surface level. Hand tools or mechanised equipment can be used.

Irrigation: watering turf. Sprinklers are often used to do this.

Turfing: the use of pre-cut pieces of turf for the establishment of a new lawn or for the repair of established lawns.

Seeding: the application of grass seed for the establishment of a new lawn or for the repair of established lawns.

 TIP

Aeration: When using Solid tines for aeration, use them for three years and then Hollow tine in the fourth year.

! ! REMEMBER

Only roll turf when necessary – too much rolling can damage turf.

Recreational Playing Surfaces

The following list represents some of the playing surfaces that use grass:

1. Bowling greens: crown green and flat green
2. Cricket pitches: cricket tables (squares) and the outfields
3. Football pitches
4. Golf Courses: 18 hole, 9 hole, pitch and putt or putting greens
5. Hockey pitches
6. Rugby pitches
7. Lawn tennis courts
8. Racecourses: flat and jump courses.

The following list shows examples of seed mixtures for use in Amenity Horticulture, ranging from lawns to winter sports pitches.

Sporting Surfaces

1. Bowling green: 75% Frida Chewings Fescue
   25% Highland Browntop Bent
   } sowing rate 35 g/m^2

2. Cricket square: 30% Loretta Perennial Ryegrass
   55% Chewings Fescue
   15% Browntop Bent
   } sowing rate 35 g/m^2

3. Cricket outfield: 20% Loretta Perennial Ryegrass
   25% Creeping Red Fescue
   20% Chewings Fescue
   20% Smooth Stalk Meadow Grass
   15% Browntop Bent
   } sowing rate 40 g/m^2

4. Football pitches: 50% Loretta Perennial Ryegrass
   25% Smooth Stalk Meadow Grass
   15% Chewings Fescue
   10% Highland Browntop Bent
   } sowing rate 40 g/m^2

5. Golf greens: as for Bowling greens
   Golf fairways: as for Football pitches
6. Hockey pitches: as for Football pitches
7. Rugby pitches: as for Football pitches
8. Lawn tennis courts: as for Cricket squares
9. Racecourses: 25% early flowering Perennial Ryegrass
   25% late flowering Perennial Ryegrass
   25% Creeping Red Fescue
   15% Smooth Stalk Meadow Grass
   10% Browntop Bent
   } sowing rate 40 g/m^2

General Amenity Areas

1. Ornamental lawn: 60% Chewings Fescue
   (viewing only) 20% Creeping Red Fescue
   20% Browntop Bent
   } sowing rate 35 g/m^2

2. Ornamental lawn: 45% Perennial Ryegrass
   (for family use) 45% Chewings Fescue
   10% Browntop Bent
   } sowing rate 35g/m^2

3. Highway verges: 20% Perennial Ryegrass
   (roads) 20% Smooth Stalk Meadow Grass
   50% Creeping Red Fescue
   10% Browntop Bent
   } sowing rate 40 g/m^2

   On road verges, particularly motorway verges, wild flower seed and white clover seed can be added to the mixture. This will aid germination and establishment on these sites.

4. Housing estates: 25% Perennial Ryegrass
   25% Smooth Stalk Meadow Grass
   40% Creeping Red Fescue
   10% Browntop Bent
   } sowing rate 40 g/m^2

Parks and Gardens

Parks and gardens are the basis of Amenity Horticulture, and probably the best examples of it. They vary in size and shape, and are all individual containing a variety of plants and facilities.

Parks

The three main types of park are:
1. Public Parks
2. Country Parks
3. National Parks.

1. *Public Parks*

Public parks are found in all Local Authority areas throughout the UK. They are run and administered by a department of the Local Authority; for example, the Parks Department, the Leisure and Recreation Department or the Amenities and Leisure Department. The titles of these departments do vary from Local Authority to Local Authority, but they all employ gardening staff for the maintenance and upkeep of Public Parks. As the name suggests, these parks exist to serve the public, to provide free pleasure gardens and, above all, to provide amenities. The number of public parks within a Local Authority will vary depending on the Authority's population. Public parks are generally located near or in busy towns or cities. The facilities each offers depends on how big the park is, together with how well it is used.

A typical town public park may contain the following facilities:

1. Long walks.
2. Adequate seating (usually in the form of benches throughout the park).
3. Playgrounds, ranging from children's play area to an adventure playground.
4. Games areas: putting greens, lawn tennis courts, football pitches, bowling greens.
5. Café (usually open during the summer).
6. Paddling pool.
7. Glasshouse/conservatory displaying houseplants.
8. Collections of trees and shrubs, herbaceous borders, bedding displays.
9. Theme gardens: rose gardens, rock gardens.
10. Toilet facilities.
11. Parking facilities.
12. Litter disposers (located at regular intervals throughout the park).

 TO DO

Visit your local public parks, and make a checklist of the facilities they offer.

! ! REMEMBER

Turf or grass has a major role to play in a public park. Could you imagine a park without grass?

Maintaining Public Parks

As you can see, public parks contain a wide variety of ornamental and recreational facilities. We have already dealt with the maintenance of many of the ornamental features in Chapter 2, and we have already looked at the maintenance of recreational areas in this chapter. We need now to look at the maintenance of one of the primary areas of a public park – the playground and play equipment.

The Maintenance of Playgrounds and Play Equipment

Traditionally, playground surfaces are made of concrete or tarmac which will do nothing to cushion a child's fall from a piece of equipment. However, many local Authorities are now beginning to look at alternative play surfaces, particularly beneath individual play equipment. For example, rubber mats and various types of forest bark are now being used.

The provision of play equipment is generally concerned with children in the 5–11 age group. Here is a variety of play equipment which might be found in a public park:

Children's play equipment

1. Swings: probably the most popular item; various sizes.
2. Merry-go-rounds: various sizes.
3. Slides: various sizes.
4. See-saws: various sizes.
5. Climbing frames: various shapes and sizes.
6. Sand pits: various shapes and sizes.
7. Rocking horses: various sizes.
8. Paddling Pools: various shapes and sizes.

All playground equipment must conform to British Standards specifications.

Playgrounds and play equipment should be regularly visited, inspected and, where necessary, maintained. The following checklist may help as a guideline.

Initial Inspection and Maintenance Checklist
1. Locate the parks throughout the authority.
2. Transport to site appropriate cleansing materials, tools and equipment associated with the maintenance of play equipment.
3. Check playground surfaces and remove dangerous materials, for example glass.
4. Check bolts, brackets, seats, chains and uprights of equipment.
5. Grease moving joints (depends on equipment).
6. Remove graffiti and check for vandalism.
7. Check sandpits.

! !   **REMEMBER**

Vandalism is a source of danger for play equipment. Regular acts of vandalism will mean your sites must be more frequently inspected.

△   **SAFETY**

Safety is of paramount importance in children's play areas.

2. *Country Parks*

As their name suggests, these parks are usually found out of the town or city and are situated in open countryside. Many Local Authorities have now set up and manage country parks in accordance with the Countryside Act. However, private landowners can also, if they wish, provide country parks. Country parks provide an opportunity for town/city people to enjoy a day out in the country without having to travel long distances. Local Authority country parks tend to be only short distances from the town/city centre, with many approach roads to avoid traffic congestion, particularly in the summer.

Country parks are generally much larger than public parks although about 20 acres (approximately 8 hectares) is regarded as a minimum size. Many country parks are many times this size. Some of the main characteristics of country parks are:

1. Large parkland areas	These areas may also
2. Heath land	include lakes, ponds,
3. Woodland	rivers, streams, livestock
4. Farmland	areas and picnic sites

Depending on the size of the Local Authority, there may be more than one country park in a particular Authority's area.

Maintaining Country Parks

The maintenance of country parks follows similar lines to those for public parks, except that there will be an obvious difference in size of the area requiring maintenance. More specialist maintenance may be needed more frequently, for example, arboricultural teams will be required for the maintenance of amenity woodlands.

New Country Parks

There is little doubt that there is a need for more parks, particularly country parks. Nowadays we do not necessarily have to look for new land – we can use old land which was formerley used for other things. New country parks can be created out of the following:

1. Disused railway lines/cuttings	
2. Disused quarries	
3. Disused gravel pits	Reclamation
4. Colliery spoil heaps	
5. Disused industrial land.	

 TO DO

Find out if your Local Authority has a country park. How big is it? Is it well used? What does it offer the visitor?

3. National Parks

National parks are administered and controlled by the Countryside Commission (previously controlled by the National Parks Commission). The Countryside Commission has the power to designate areas of unspoilt natural beauty. From 1951 to 1957 the following ten National Parks were designated (in order of designation):

1. Peak District (England)
2. Lake District (England)
3. Snowdonia (Wales)
4. Dartmoor (England)
5. Pembrokeshire Coast (Wales)
6. North Yorkshire Moors (England)
7. Yorkshire Dales (England)
8. Exmoor (England)
9. Northumberland (England)
10. Brecon Beacons (Wales)

} The National Parks cover about 9% of the area of England and Wales.

National Parks are often defined as: an extensive area of beautiful and relatively wild countryside set aside for the nation's benefit.

Because of the size of these parks, the Countryside Commission works closely with the following organisations:

1. County Councils/Local Authorities
2. Nature Conservancy Council
3. Forestry Commission
4. National Trust
5. Private Landowners.

Once a National Park has become designated land, ownership within the park does not change, for example a farmer will still own and occupy his/her land. National Park land is therefore owned by numerous people and organisations; it is most definitely not public property, which means the right of access is not always automatic.

> **! ! REMEMBER**
>
> There are many more organisations which help the Commission in the upkeep of National Parks.

Maintaining National Parks

To make the running of the parks easier, each park is locally managed by either a National Park Board or by County Council Committees. The Government makes funds available towards the administration and upkeep of the parks. National Parks have their own Advisors and Wardens and many volunteer workers helping to keep the parks in good order. Each local management board prepares its own national park plan; in this way they can control events and new developments within the park boundary.

Many of the parks have information centres which help to make sure that visitors make the most of their time in the park.

Gardens

Gardens come in all shapes and sizes and can be found in many different locations. In both the public and private sectors, gardens are often given names which tell us exactly what they are used for. Here are some of the names given to gardens:

1. Pleasure gardens: usually large gardens to walk around and admire.
2. Rose gardens
3. Flower gardens
4. Fruit gardens
5. Vegetable gardens
6. Herb gardens
7. Cottage gardens: an old style garden, growing a mixture of plants.
8. Woodland gardens: a collection of trees and woodland type plants.
9. Rock gardens: a garden growing alpines, rock plants and associated plants.
10. Water gardens: a garden showing off aquatics, marginals and fish.
11. Memorial gardens: gardens that commemorate events or people's lives.
12. Walled gardens: the wall provides shelter for the growing of various plants.
13. Bird gardens: a garden housing a collection of birds.
14. Tea gardens: a place in which to take tea in the open.
15. Gardens for the disabled: specially designed and built gardens for disabled people.
16. Gardens for the blind: specially designed gardens, containing highly scented plants.
17. Theme gardens: for example, a Japanese garden.
18. Kitchen gardens: a garden historically used for the growing of various food crops.
19. Miniature gardens: gardens set out in miniature.
20. Gardens of remembrance: similar to memorial gardens.

Gardens in the Public Sector

As well as having parks, Local Authorities have numerous small gardens which are sited throughout the district. Their upkeep and maintenance follows similar guidelines to those of the park. These gardens are invaluable to the public and are generally well used.

 TO DO

Find out how many gardens your Local Authority has.
Are they of a similar design?
What plants are grown?

Gardens in the Private Sector

Gardens in this sector are usually on a large scale, merging into parkland and woodland surrounds. The gardens themselves are presented either formally or informally, and frequently a particularly large garden can present both. The majority of these gardens belong to the National Trust, or they are still in the ownership of titled families. During the year, and in some cases all year round, the gardens are open to the public (for the majority of them, admission charges are made). To maintain the gardens, the National Trust employs a team of resident gardeners (the numbers will vary, depending on the size of the garden). In the case of private ownership, a team of resident gardeners can be employed or landscape contractors may be brought in. A combination of the two is also frequently used. Many of these large gardens have and continue to have a role to play in garden history. The National Trust has some of the best preserved historical gardens in the UK, for example, Stowe in Buckinghamshire or Hidcote in Gloucestershire. National collections of plants are also to be found in large gardens of the private sector.

TO DO

Divide the UK into North, South, East and West. Make a list of five private gardens to be found in each area.
How many do you already know?

Dealing with the Public

Staff in the public sector need to be aware of their department's policies, procedures and by-laws. In a similar way staff in the private sector should be aware of rules and regulations of the garden or estate. In both sectors, staff should communicate well with the public, promote the department or garden, advise on queries raised and generally be as helpful as possible. Where tickets are issued (for admissions), staff should be numerate and able to complete forms and records efficiently.

4 | ARBORICULTURE

Trees and Tree Planting

Amenity Trees

Arboriculture is the study of amenity trees. Such trees play a vital role in our environment: they adorn our streets, parks and gardens, and make our landscape much more interesting. This type of tree is not planted for its timber and so has no resale commercial value. The trees in this group are amenity trees. Aboriculture therefore is the part of Amenity Horticulture concerned with the establishment, cultivation, maintenance and management of amenity trees.

The Value of Trees

All trees are valuable, but their value is not simply money or profit. Trees have much more to offer than just being grown as a commodity for sale, which is the basis of commercial production or forestry. Amenity trees have many environmental values, which are often taken for granted.

All trees, whether grown commercially for profit or planted as amenity trees, contribute to the environment. Trees help to clean the atmosphere, and provide oxygen and habitats for wildlife, to name but three of their functions. Their value and contributions to the environment are manifold, each just as important as the rest.

Here are some of the most important functions of amenity trees:

1. They help to soften the landscape and enhance the look of open spaces.
2. They help to judge scale and distance, particularly around buildings.
3. They screen unsightly buildings or objects.
4. They absorb noise and filter dust and fumes.
5. They provide an assortment of interesting shapes and sizes.
6. They enhance our environment through their flowers, leaf colour, bark and fruits.
7. They provide shelter and habitats for wildlife.

Amenity tree in a garden setting

 TO DO

Make a list, complete with sketches, of six trees with different shapes.

Some common tree shapes

Weeping or Pendulous   Columnar or Fastigate   Conical

74

For most of us, living and working in the urban environment, forests are not an everyday part of our lives, yet, by careful planning and planting, we are able to soften our harsh surroundings with trees.

Street trees

Selecting and planting amenity trees is very important; it would be quite easy to plant the wrong tree in any given situation. Try to understand an individual tree's life expectancy, habit, growth rate, and you will discover what it requires for healthy growth and development.

Technical Information

A tree is both perennial and woody. Trees can be divided into two distinct groups – deciduous or coniferous.

The majority of amenity trees will grow on a wide range of soils but there are exceptions. When deciding on a planting plan or even if you are only to plant one tree, check the pH of your soil; this will tell you whether it is acid or alkaline. Such information is often vital to the establishment and growth of trees.

 SAFETY

Street trees
Regular maintenance is essential to keep them in good order and to make sure they are safe to both road users and pedestrians alike.

X   **USEFUL TERMS**

Deciduous The mainly broadleaved trees that drop their leaves in autumn. Broadleaved trees are often referred to as hardwoods. Individual varieties range from short to very tall.
Coniferous A cone-bearing plant, the majority of which are evergreen. Conifer trees are often referred to as softwoods. They have an extensive height range, depending on individual variety.
Evergreens Species that retain their leaves in winter. The majority of conifers belong to this group. Remember, not all evergreens are conifers.

 TO DO

pH test
Using a proprietary soil pH kit, carry out a pH test and from it assess the practicality of the soil against the tree or trees you wish to plant. You may find you have to alter your choice of tree or trees.

Siting Trees

Before any planting takes place, you will need to decide on a suitable site. Young trees are vulnerable to the effects of both climate and aspect, which must be considered carefully prior to buying them. Even though the majority of trees, including conifers, are hardy, they are not all perfectly tolerant of climate and aspect. Persistent strong winds or severe frosts will almost certainly damage many species through the course of their lives. This damage is increased if the tree is planted in the wrong situation.

Tree Specifications

The British Standards Institution produces numerous specifications for trees, which serve as a good guide to growers and consumers alike.

The British Standards Institution and British Container Growers Specification of Standards *BS3936* provides information on the following:

1. Origin
2. Root system
3. Condition
4. Packaging
5. Labelling
6. Standard trees
7. Feathered trees
8. Whip
9. Bush tree
10. Transplant
11. Seedling
12. Conifers

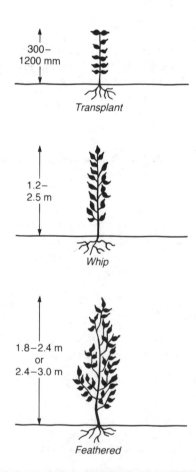

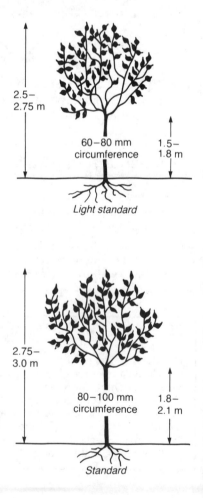

Tree categories and specifications (courtesy of the Horticultural Trades Association)

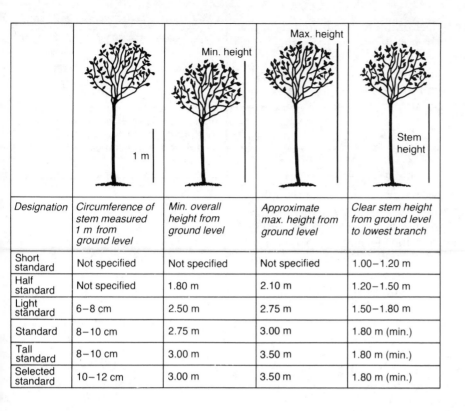

Designation	Circumference of stem measured 1 m from ground level	Min. overall height from ground level	Approximate max. height from ground level	Clear stem height from ground level to lowest branch
Short standard	Not specified	Not specified	Not specified	1.00–1.20 m
Half standard	Not specified	1.80 m	2.10 m	1.20–1.50 m
Light standard	6–8 cm	2.50 m	2.75 m	1.50–1.80 m
Standard	8–10 cm	2.75 m	3.00 m	1.80 m (min.)
Tall standard	8–10 cm	3.00 m	3.50 m	1.80 m (min.)
Selected standard	10–12 cm	3.00 m	3.50 m	1.80 m (min.)

Dimensions of standard trees (courtesy of the Horticultural Trades Association)

Designation	Circumference of stem measured 1 m from ground level	Min. overall height from ground level	Max. overall height from ground level	Clear stem height from ground level to lowest branch
Seedling	—	—	—	—
Transplant	—	—	1.20 m	—
Whip	— — — —	1.20 m 1.50 m 1.80 m 2.10 m	1.50 m 1.80 m 2.10 m 2.50 m	— — — —
Feathered	— — —	1.80 m 2.10 m 2.50 m	2.10 m 2.50 m 3.00 m	— — —
Bush	—	—	—	30–60 cm

Dimensions of other tree forms (courtesy of the Horticultural Trades Association)

Designation	Circumference of stem measured 1 m from ground level	Min. overall height from ground level	Approximate max. height from ground level	Clear stem height from ground level to lowest branch
BS 5236 Advanced Nursery stock Heavy Extra heavy	12–14 cm 14–16 cm 16–18 cm 18–20 cm	3.60 m 4.25 m — —	4.25 m 6.00 m — —	1.80 m min. 1.80 m min. 1.80 m min. 1.80 m min.
BS 4043 Semi mature	20–75 cm	6.00 m	15.00 m	Not specified

Dimensions of more advanced tree forms (courtesy of the Horticultural Trades Association)

Amenity trees provide us with a great deal of interest year round, and we will gain most if they are given the best possible start. Trees that are planted as street trees especially require this, and hence they often need a good deal of care and attention. The soil in which they are to be planted may well be poor, badly drained or even not deep enough. This can lead to major problems in their establishment, but if we anticipate the problems they may be overcome easily.

Establishment of trees

Trees of various species, shapes and sizes are regularly used in landscaping projects ranging from pedestrian precincts through to motorway verges and parkland. The terminology for the size and age of trees often varies, however, three professional terms used for the developing plants are: *forestry seedlings* (seedling plants), *nursery stock* (young plants), and *semi-mature* (older plant, 10 years or more, depending on the tree).

One other criterion directly affecting the planting of trees is just how they have been grown. In this respect, the choice is generally field-grown or container-grown, however, it is possible to have a combination of both. In the case of field-grown trees, they may be planted as bare-rooted or root balled plants, usually in the dormant season. Container-grown plants can be planted throughout the year, provided planting conditions are suitable and that the necessary post-planting criteria can be successfully carried out (irrigation for example).

Prior to planting, keep bare-rooted trees moist and prevent them from drying out. The trees can be temporarily heeled in and planted at an angle of about 45°, the roots being covered with damp compost or soil.

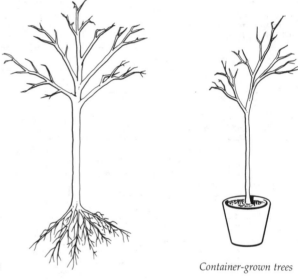

Bare rooted trees

Container-grown trees

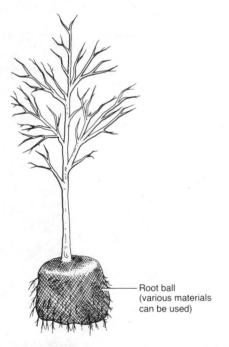

Root ball
(various materials
can be used)

Root-balled trees

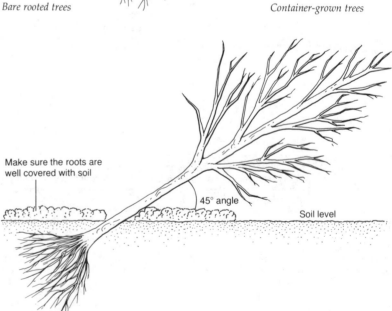

Make sure the roots are
well covered with soil

45° angle

Soil level

Heeling-in trees

⚠ **SAFETY**

Think about the size that street trees will grow to. Will this cause problems? Take into account traffic, underground service pipes, and the various aerial services. Remember, both root growth and top growth could lead to difficulties in the future.

Preparing and Planting on Site

Whether you are planting seedlings, standard or semi-mature trees, preparation of the planting site is the key to establishing the tree successfully. Generally you will need to check and then locate any mains services there might be on site. You must do this before any preparations begin. Decide on appropriate tools, equipment and soil ameliorants (or improvers) you need, and have them all on site as required. Site preparation should take the form of a series of set objectives, completed in order as a sequence of events. Many of these preparatory stages are covered by British Standard specifications, so refer to them prior to doing the job.

The following ten-point plan (intended for a standard tree) helps to put site preparations and planting into perspective.

1. Select the site (where possible make a plan of the site – it will aid planting).
2. Remove surface debris and obstacles from the site and mark out a circle of about 1 m diameter.
3. Take out the top soil and pile it separately ⎫ to a total depth
4. Take out the sub-soil and pile it separately ⎭ of about 600 mm.
5. Fork over the bottom of the pit and mix in the soil ameliorants, FYM for example, raising the level slightly.
6. Holding the tree and stake together, check their relative positions in the planting pit. Remember, ideally the stake needs to be on the windward side of the tree.
7. Secure the stake in its position.
8. Plant the tree, making sure that it is only up to its previous planting depth or soil line. At this stage, check and remove any damaged roots or branches as required. Backfill and firm the soil as necessary.
9. Secure the tree to the stake using appropriate tree ties, usually two per standard tree. The top of the stake ideally should be just below the bottom branch.
10. The site should be left clean and tidy. Return all equipment to store after it has been cleaned as required.

 TIP

When preparing the tree pit, separate the top soil from the sub-soil. When backfilling, begin with your top soil.

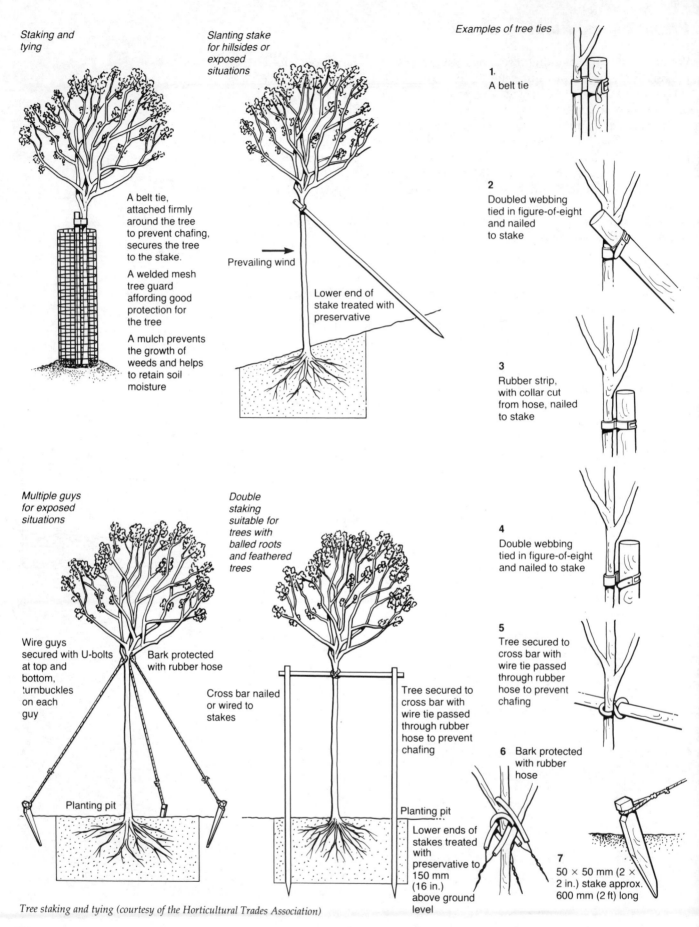

Staking and tying

A belt tie, attached firmly around the tree to prevent chafing, secures the tree to the stake.

A welded mesh tree guard affording good protection for the tree

A mulch prevents the growth of weeds and helps to retain soil moisture

Slanting stake for hillsides or exposed situations

Prevailing wind

Lower end of stake treated with preservative

Examples of tree ties

1.
A belt tie

2
Doubled webbing tied in figure-of-eight and nailed to stake

3
Rubber strip, with collar cut from hose, nailed to stake

4
Double webbing tied in figure-of-eight and nailed to stake

5
Tree secured to cross bar with wire tie passed through rubber hose to prevent chafing

6 Bark protected with rubber hose

7
50 × 50 mm (2 × 2 in.) stake approx. 600 mm (2 ft) long

Multiple guys for exposed situations

Wire guys secured with U-bolts at top and bottom, turnbuckles on each guy

Bark protected with rubber hose

Planting pit

Double staking suitable for trees with balled roots and feathered trees

Cross bar nailed or wired to stakes

Tree secured to cross bar with wire tie passed through rubber hose to prevent chafing

Planting pit

Lower ends of stakes treated with preservative to 150 mm (16 in.) above ground level

Tree staking and tying (courtesy of the Horticultural Trades Association)

When to Plant Trees

The two main types of tree have different optimal planting times.

1. Deciduous species are planted from mid October and throughout the winter up until March if the weather is suitable. Planting is ideally therefore, in the dormant season.
2. Evergreen species are planted either in the autumn or in spring. For planting of evergreen species, the condition of the soil is vital; the soil needs to be warm and, given moist aerial conditions, evergreens can be successfully planted.

Trees, whether they are seedlings, nursery stock or even semi-mature trees, need to be protected before planting both on site and in transit. If the correct procedures are not undertaken at either stage, the tree may well not be successfully established.

All trees, irrespective of size and age, will require maintenance after planting. This maintenance will obviously vary, depending on the tree. Here are the main criteria which affect the majority of trees.

1. Use the appropriate or recommended protection. For seedlings, nursery stock and semi-mature trees, refer to the relevant British Standards specifications on tree protection.
2. Ideally, mulch each tree using a suitable mulching material. Again, reference to appropriate British Standard specifications would help.
3. Irrigation is vital in most instances to the successful establishment of trees. Check the relevant British Standard specifications for recommendations.
4. Check the tree throughout its formative years. Check for growth and development, die-back, dead or diseased material and, where necessary, vandalism. This may or may not lead to a re-planting programme in due course.

> **!! REMEMBER**
>
> If the tree is container grown, whether it is deciduous or evergreen, you can plant it at any time of the year. However, conditions need to be suitable and irrigation will be needed to aid establishment.

> **!! REMEMBER**
>
> Check and alter or remove tree ties as the tree grows.

Tree guard on a standard tree

Tree vandalism

Amenity Woodlands

Establishing amenity woodlands is a long process, which in many cases takes more than a life-time. It would be much easier to take over an existing woodland and develop it into an amenity woodland. Probably the best example of an amenity woodland is a woodland garden. Woodland gardens are very important features. Here are some of their functions:

1. To grow and exhibit a mixed selection of trees, for them to be seen and admired and not just grown for their timber.
2. To form a canopy for shade-loving plants.
3. To provide a suitable habit for specific woodland plants.
4. To provide a habitat for wildlife.
5. Nature trails can be made through woodlands providing an educational resource.

Tree Selection (a guide to establishment)
When selecting trees for a woodland garden, choose plants from a whole range of trees sizes – for example, 1-year-old whips to extra-heavy standards or semi-mature trees. In this way you will also have a diversity of age just as you would have in a natural woodland. Also, it is important to use a mixture of deciduous and evergreen species; not only will this give you a more interesting woodland, it will also help in the control of pests and diseases.

Your selection should include a number of quick growing species such as willows or alders; these trees can be grown close together to begin with, and thinned out at a later date. Quick growing species will help you attain cover in a short time. A shady environment is critical for the success of many woodland plants.

Trees – Examples

Deciduous species

Acer campestre
Betula pendula
Malus floribunda
Prunus 'Kanzan'
Sorbus aria

Evergreen species

Cryptomeria japonica
Chamaecyparis species
Ilex aquifolium
Eucalyptus species
Quercus ilex

Trees with coloured foliage

Acer palmatum 'Atropurpureum' (purple)
Acer pseudoplatanus 'Brilliantissimum' (variegated)
Acer pseudoplatanus 'Worleei' (yellow)
Acer japonicum 'Aureum' (yellow)
Chamaecyparis lawsoniana 'Stewartii' (yellow)
Ilex x altaclarensis 'Golden King' (variegated)
Fagus sylvatica purpurea 'Riversii' (purple)
Malus 'Profusion' (purple)
Prunus cerasifera 'Nigra' (purple)
Robinia pseudoacacia 'Frisia' (yellow)
Eucalytpus gunnii (grey)
Pyrus salicifolia 'Pendula' (silver)
Cedrus atlantica 'Glauca' (blue)
Populus x candicans 'Aurora' (variegated)

Trees for autumn colour

Amelanchier canadensis
Liquidambar styraciflua
Malus tschonoskii
Parrotia persica
Prunus sargentii

Good flowering trees

Cercis siliquastrum
Crataegus oxycantha
'Rosea Flore Pleno'
Prunus 'Kanzan'
Prunus subhirtella 'Autumnalis'
Laburnum watereri 'Vossii'

Tree habits

(a) Fastigiate trees

Acer saccharinum 'Pyramidale'
Carpinus betulus 'Columnaris'
Liriodendron tulipifera 'Fastigiatum'
Populus nigra 'Italica'
Prunus 'Amanogawa'

(b) Pendulous trees

Betula pendula 'Youngii'
Fagus sylvatica 'Pendula'
Pyrus salicifolia 'Pendula'
Salix chrysocoma
Salix matsudana 'Pendula'

Trees with ornamental bark

Acer griseum
Betula species
Eucalyptus species
Prunus serrula
Platanus species

Trees bearing ornamental fruit

Arbutus unedo
Catalpa bignonioides
Ilex species
Malus 'Golden Hornet'
Sorbus 'Joseph Rock'

Trees with scented flowers

Crataegus monogyna
Malus floribunda
Malus 'Profusion'
Tilia x euchlora
Tilia petiolaris

Winter-flowering trees

Populus tremula
Prunus incisa 'Praecox'
Acer rubrum
Prunus subhirtella
Magnolia species

Summer-flowering trees

Castanea sativa
Catalpa bignonioides
Koelreuteria paniculata
Liriodendron tulipifera
Magnolia delavayi

Spring-flowering trees

Amelanchier canadensis
Crataegus species
Davidia involucrata
Malus species
Prunus species

Autumn-flowering trees

Eucryphia x nymansensis
Prunus subhirtella 'Autumnalis'

Trees suitable for coastal areas

Arbutus unedo
Crataegus species
Ilex aquifolium
Populus alba
Sorbus aucuparia

Trees tolerant of alkaline soils

Acer griseum
Acer negundo
Betula species (may not reach their maximum height on these soils)
Fagus species
Sorbus aria

Trees tolerant of acid soils

Acer rubrum
Castanea species
Cercis species
Koelreuteria paniculata
Ilex aquifolium

Trees for wet sites

Alnus species
Amelanchier species
Populus species
Salix species

Trees for exposed sites

Acer pseudoplatanus cultivars
Betula pendula
Laburnum species
Sorbus aria
Sorbus intermedia

 TO DO

Looking at the lists, design a small arboretum that would provide all-year-round interest.

Tree Maintenance

Weed, Pest and Disease Control

Weeds, pests and diseases will all affect the successful establishment of trees, whether they are seedlings planted on a motorway verge or standard trees planted in a park. We need to bear in mind that trees will be attacked by all three during their establishment, so that we can therefore take appropriate preventive action. Clearly, the first steps are to recognise and identify the problem.

Following the recommendations and guidelines set down by the Food and Environmental Protection Act 1985 (FEPA), select and then prepare your recommended control method. Following the manufacturer's instructions, you can then apply the control accordingly.

Knapsack sprayer

Chemical store

Tree Pruning

Tree pruning in many cases is an essential maintenance operation if trees are to be kept in a healthy and safe manner. Pruning can be considered a growth-controlling operation, as it will effectively control a tree's ability to grow, flower and fruit. As the tree gets older, the pruning can become more difficult. Pruning is vital while the tree is young and is considered essential to its growth.

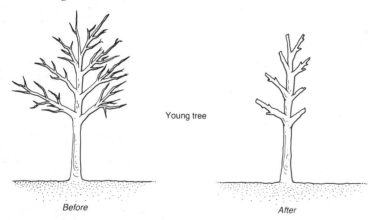

Young tree

Before

After

Pruning young nursery trees

The above diagrams show an example of formative pruning, vital to the formation of a good branch framework while still in the nursery.

⚠ **SAFETY**

Safety precautions need to be taken on all planting sites. Where appropriate, use warning signs or barriers; these should be in position before any digging commences.
  Lighting may be required if works cannot be completed in daylight.

▶▶▶ **TO DO**

Look around your working environment or even your garden, and identify some of the common problems. Make a list of your findings. How could you control them?

⚠ **SAFETY**

The application of pesticides can be dangerous for untrained people. Ask your college about the FEPA recommendations on training and competence testing.

⚠ **SAFETY**

All chemicals must be correctly stored and kept under lock and key. All equipment and unused materials should be cleaned and then returned to the store as appropriate.

Climbing

The climber needs to ascend the tree in a safe manner according to the relevant British Standard specifications and associated guidelines. Identified branches for pruning need to be secured before pruning starts; once pruning has been carried out, branches are lowered using only recommended techniques. By following British Standard guidelines throughout the operation, the task should be completed in a safe and appropriate manner. Finally, the climber will need to descend the tree safely.

Pruning

There are two types of tree pruning: ground pruning and off-the-ground pruning. In ground pruning, the trees are pruned from the ground using appropriate tools and equipment, including the necessary protective clothing. Select the appropriate branches and prune them; then clear the prunings and any other debris from the site.

A collection of small trees

For off-the-ground pruning, you must climb the tree. Climbers must identify the branches to be pruned and prepare themselves for all the aspects of the job. You need formal training and guidance for off-the-ground pruning.

Why prune trees?

It has already been explained why trees are pruned in the nursery. Once a tree begins to grow and develop after it is established, many trees, particularly those used as street trees, will require pruning as a part of their maintenance programme. Many of the principles described for tree pruning can be used on other plants to achieve the same aims and objectives.

⚠ **SAFETY**

Check:
Climbing equipment, ropes, harness belts etc.
Pruning tools and equipment
Method of climb
Anchor points
Groundperson in attendance
Secure area beneath the tree.

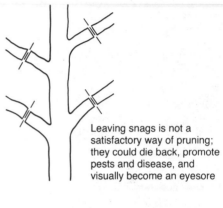

Leaving snags is not a satisfactory way of pruning; they could die back, promote pests and disease, and visually become an eyesore

Pruning this way leaves not too much of a snag and not too much of a wound

Tree pruning

PRUNING

Wrong

Leaving snags is not a satisfactory way of pruning branches. They could die back, promote pests and diseases and are visually an eyesore.

Right

Leave a clean cut close to the main stem or limb as appropriate. This will promote callusing and not hinder it.

Correct removal of a branch

85

The following list represents some of the main reasons for pruning trees.

1. To promote the development of a balanced crown.
2. For safety reasons: removal of branches from service cables; to lift the crown of the tree to give clearance to passing traffic; branches may interfere with buildings; branches may be unsafe and potentially dangerous.
3. To remove the three 'D's: dead, diseased and dying wood.
4. To reduce a tree's total leaf surface, so benefiting the root system by decreasing the demands on it for water and nutrients.
5. To improve aeration inside the tree canopy, which will lessen the risk of disease.
6. To maintain a good tree shape (by using appropriate thinning techniques) and allow better light transmission, particularly when trees are close to buildings.
7. Careful and thoughtful pruning enhances the overall look of the tree and helps keep it healthy.

All trees are not pruned in the same way or at the same time of the year. To understand pruning, an understanding of tree science and pruning techniques together with a good knowledge of species are essential. Suitable training courses promote this understanding.

✳ FOR INTEREST

British Standard specifications and numbers for arboricultural work can be obtained from the British Standards Institution, 2 Park Street, London, W1A 2BS.

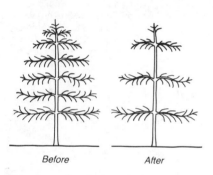

Before *After*

Thinning out standard/established trees

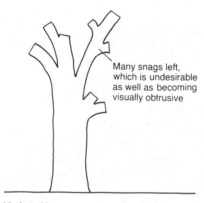

Many snags left, which is undesirable as well as becoming visually obtrusive

Undesirable tree pruning

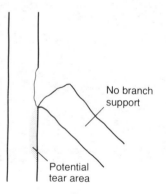

No branch support

Potential tear area

The wrong way

Undesirable pruning

The diagram shows tree mutilation. This type of pruning is known as lopping or pollarding. While it can be effective with certain plant species, for example *Buddleia*, it is an undesirable practice for trees. Apart from the tree becoming visually obtrusive, often (depending on species) a profusion of growth results, probably causing more of a problem than it did before it was pruned. This type of pruning can lead to the death of some species, *Betula* and *Fagus* species for example.

Making the cut

Where thin (less than 25 mm) branches are concerned, a light pruning saw or secateurs can be used. In the case of larger branches, the weight of each branch should be taken off prior to pruning; this should then produce a clean cut. A larger handsaw or chainsaw is generally used for this operation.

For branches that need to be taken down in sections, if the undercut is made first this will reduce tearing. Leave the final branch section fairly short (about 250 mm).

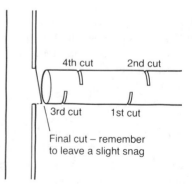

4th cut   2nd cut

3rd cut   1st cut

Final cut – remember to leave a slight snag

The right way

Branch removal

Cavities

Cavities are a constant problem in trees – they can be found in their trunks, branches and forks. Cavities are holes or hollows usually formed by external or internal means, which cause the tree to rot and decay. The decaying is often accelerated by numerous fungi and bacteria. Cavities can be sucessfully treated and controlled if they are caught early. Cavity repair, however, is a skilful and expensive operation. It should also be remembered that cavities come in all shapes and sizes, are time-consuming to repair, the work being governed by a number of safety factors.

⚠ **SAFETY**

Some cavities, because of their inaccessibility, may not be repairable. In such cases, the tree should be felled if it is considered a safety hazard.

Tree cavity

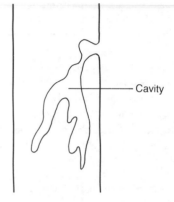

Unaccessible trunk cavity

Where cavities are accessible and safe to work on, fillers can be used according to the relevant British Standard recommendations. However, think carefully, as very often rotting may continue under the filling; this will lead to difficulties later on. Inaccessible cavities, however, are in some respects a little easier to deal with. Provided a reasonable amount of cleaning can be done (this may involve widening the entrance hole), a mesh and drainage pipe will certainly help.

Draining a Cavity
Use some type of probe or yardstick to assess the depth of the cavity. This is vital to the placement of the drainage pipe.

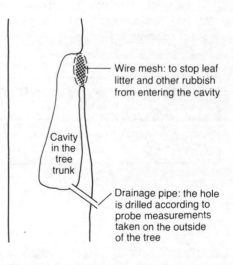

Wire mesh: to stop leaf litter and other rubbish from entering the cavity

Cavity in the tree trunk

Drainage pipe: the hole is drilled according to probe measurements taken on the outside of the tree

Draining a tree cavity

Tree Felling

Tree felling, or cutting trees to the ground, is a task which must be done competently and in a safe manner. A tree can be felled in a single piece or reduced in a series of sections. The location of the tree will dictate which method should be used. Trees are felled for a variety of reasons, such as safety, site clearance and hygiene.

▶ ▶ ▶   **TO DO**

Using the general headings given to you, make a list of examples influencing the felling of trees.

! !   **REMEMBER**

Amenity trees grown as a small woodland may need some thinning from time to time. Very often such thinnings can have a commercial timber value.

Where trees are situated in an open site such as a field, the operation is quite straightforward. Here the appropriate tool would be a reasonably sized chainsaw. On restricted sites, the tree is best felled in stages; this will involve branch lowering using appropriate ropes. The climber has to work with the groundperson; it is essential for the task to be performed in a safe manner.

△   **SAFETY**

When felling trees, you must observe safe working practices. Consult the relevant British Standard recommendations.

! !   **REMEMBER**

Be trained in tree felling. Ask your college about appropriate courses.

Treating Cuts and Repairing Wounds

The painting of wounds or cuts is no longer acceptable after pruning, since it is an ineffective practice. Treatments concerned with other protective methods are currently being researched. In any event, at the moment, wound sealants for pruning trees are not acceptable.

    TO DO

Make a list of trees that could bleed badly if pruned at the wrong time of year. You may be surprised at the number of common trees that fall into this category.

Supporting Limbs

There are various methods of supporting trees, based on bracing, propping or both. These techniques help support a tree's branch or branches and give strength to weak or potentially weak areas. If correctly used, they can save or prolong the life of a tree. However, safety has to come first, and you must think carefully before carrying out such work. The work itself is expensive and can lead to costly future maintenance and checking.

Propping is a technique for supporting low branches of large trees or small trees that lean for some reason. Props are usually made of wood or metal, but in either case you must regularly inspect for rot in wooden props or rusting in metal props.

Tree Nutrition

Just like any other plant, trees require a balanced food supply if they cannot easily obtain food from the soil – for example, if the soil is poor or lacking in nutrients, fertiliser application will be needed. If there is any doubt as to what feed should be applied, a soil nutrient test can be carried out; this will indicate what foods the soil is short in. From this, it should be relatively easy to assess the type and measure of food to apply.

Trees will benefit most from slow release fertilisers, as fertilisers which release their elements quickly may have a detrimental effect on growth. Nitrogen, if released quickly, could produce soft growth which in turn is more likely to be attacked by pests or diseases.

The types of fertilisers used are:

1. *Bulky organic manures* (BOM) such as farmyard manure. These contain only a little plant food. Their real advantage is that they can improve a soil's physical condition. They should be applied in the spring.
2. *Liquid fertilisers*. These are fairly quick acting. They should be applied in the spring.
3. *Solid fertilisers* (concentrates). These are mainly compounds containing several nutrients. They should be applied in the spring.
4. *Foliar feeds*. These are taken in by the tree's foliage, and are a quick and easy way of providing a plant with food. They are often applied to young trees as an aid to establishment. Application as and when appropriate.

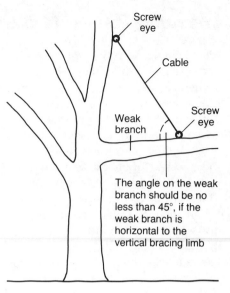

Supporting a weak branch

⚠	**SAFETY**

You will need to have received adequate training on cable bracing before attempting any such work. Ask your college about courses.

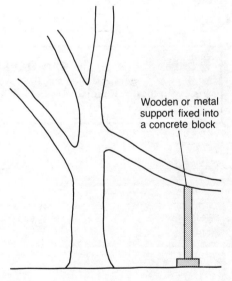

Propping a branch

Preventing Pests and Diseases

Just like other woody plants, trees can be attacked by a wide range of pests and diseases. While trees can be attacked at any time, they are particularly vulnerable at planting time and just before final establishment. Help to reduce pest and disease attack by making sure the tree(s) are planted correctly and at the right time of year. You should aim to plant your tree once only, and in the position you require. After planting, maintenance is of vital importance; irrigation, for example, in dry conditions is crucial to the survival of many trees. If trees are not properly maintained after planting they often become weak, lose vigour and have a poor appearance. Trees in this condition are more open to attack from pests and diseases. When planting, place good healthy stock in well prepared ground and draw up a maintenance programme, with pests and diseases particularly in mind. Look after your trees and adopt good cultural management techniques, although it may be impossible or impracticable to avoid certain pests or diseases. However, if you work on the principle 'prevention is better than cure', your trees should do reasonably well.

 TO DO

Make a list of 20 deciduous and coniferous trees. For each individual species, find out what pests and diseases will attack it. What control measures could you adopt?

Tree Preservation Orders

Often known as TPOs, these are used extensively today for the management and conservation of amenity trees, particularly specimen trees. TPOs are granted through the Town and Country Planning Act 1971, and are administered usually by the Planning Department of a Local Authority. Essentially, TPOs impose restrictions on the owners/occupiers of land on which the tree or trees stand.

 TO DO

Visit your local planning office and ask for information on TPOs, or write to the Arboricultural Association.

Tree Law

Amenity trees are subject to a number of laws (Common Law); these laws are concerned with the ownership of trees. We have already seen that amenity trees are planted not only in gardens and parks but in streets and at roadsides. Inevitably at some point in their life unless they have been well maintained, there will be disputes in one form or another. The law states that a tree is part of the land on which it is growing. Therefore the owner of that land is legally responsible for any trees on it, unless the land is tenanted; in this event, legal advice should be sought.

Boundary Trees

1. Trees that overhang a boundary and therefore encroach onto neighbouring property do not become a liability to the owner unless damage results.
2. If the neighbour so wishes, he/she can remove the encroaching branches. But care must be taken not to cause any damage; all cuts should be up to the boundary edge only.
3. Once the offending branches have been cut off, the neighbour must remember that the branches are not his/her property. The branches can be collected by the owner if he/she so wishes. The only other alternative to this is for the owner to give written permission for the neighbour or a contractor to dispose of the branches.
4. Fruit trees – branches that overhang a boundary and that bear fruit are liable to the same laws as in (3) above.

Tree Roots

1. If trees are planted close to a boundary, it would be reasonable to suppose that their roots at some time would encroach onto neighbouring land. As with overhanging branches, the owner of the tree is not liable unless damage caused by the roots can be proven.
2. The neighbour can, however, cut back the encroaching roots up to the boundary edge in much the same way as branches can be cut back.

5 | GARDEN DESIGN

Designing Amenity Areas

Garden and Landscape Design, in all its various forms, can be seen all around us from a small domestic garden to large landscaped sites such as reclamation sites. People have designed gardens throughout recorded time. The Romans, for example, brought gardening to Northern Europe, together with a range of designs, and introduced many plants. Before we look at the basics of garden design, I would like to summarise its development. We need to look back at garden history, in particular the influences different countries have had on design.

A Brief Garden History

After the decline of the Roman Empire, gardening did not really progress until the Middle Ages (1050–1450) when the Herb Garden was developed. After the Middle Ages, gardening began to develop once again, producing three centuries of European influences.

1. *The Italian Influence – 16th century*
The classic Italian garden was designed alongside the building/house, the main design features being semicircles, avenues and unity. The main materials used were marble, evergreens, water and pockets of bright colour. The most famous and preserved example is at Isola Bella on Lake Maggiore in northern Italy.

2. *The French Influence – 17th century*
Grand and large French gardens were inside the walls of moated châteaux. The early designs were based on Italian ideas.

Le Nôtre's 'parterre' – an intricate ground pattern ideally viewed from raised walls or balconies – was introduced. Box hedging (*Buxus*) was used for the basis of this design.

3. *The English Influence – 18th century*
This introduced interesting shapes and features, such as mounds and arbours, to gardens. Two important garden styles were developed in this era:

(a) The landscape style,
(b) The cottage style.

The most famous English landscape designer of this era is Lancelot ('Capability') Brown.

The Orient began to influence garden design during this period in three important ways:

(a) China – landscape in miniature,
(b) Japan – garden symbolism in miniature landscapes,
(c) India – water features.

Garden Designers of the Past

From the French influence

During the 17th century, France was the most affluent part of Europe and the most famous of the French garden designers was André le Nôtre, 1613–1700. His famous French gardens include Vaux le Vincomte and the garden at Versailles. Hampton Court in London was designed in the French style in 1660.

Features of Le Nôtre's designs are:

1. the garden can be seen easily from the house;
2. good use is made of vistas and fountains;
3. pathways are constructed to form patterns;
4. the use of a symmetrical style encompassing the 'parterre' and the more elaborate 'parterre de broderie';
5. many vantage points, often creating avenues, are included.

From the English influence

In the 18th century the Landscape movement developed led by three important landscape designers.

(a) William Kent, 1684–1748

Kent designed houses and gardens and was responsible for producing the sunken fence known as the 'ha ha'. His gardens were generally informal. His most famous work is at Stowe in Buckinghamshire.

(b) Lancelot Brown, 1715–1783

Brown worked under Kent at Stowe. He later moved to London and asked for design commissions. Having looked at a site he would say "it has great capabilities" hence he got the name 'Capability' Brown. His work centred around informal landscapes and examples can be found at Hampton Court, London; Temple Newsam, Leeds; Blenheim Palace, Oxford; and Harewood House, Leeds.

(c) Humphry Repton, 1752–1818

An early and successful gardens consultant, Repton's work was mainly concerned with the formal garden, with an emphasis on formality around the house. He later teamed up with John Nash (an architect) to design the famous Brighton Pavilion.

In the 19th century, J.C. Loudon – a garden designer and writer – designed the first public town park: the Arboretum at Derby, in 1840.

Planning a Garden

Before you can do any serious design work, you will need to undertake a period of planning. During this time, you must evaluate your requirements. Planning should be carried out whether you are making a new garden from scratch or you are altering an existing garden. It is very important to put some ideas down on paper and look at your site with a view to the following constraints:

(a) Site limitations – for example, size or shape of plot, soil type, sun traps or the direction of the prevailing wind.
(b) Type of garden– formal or informal.
(c) Time   – how long the garden will take to construct or how long it will take before the garden matures.
(d) Cost   – find out your budget allowance.

To help you evaluate design requirements it is advisable to draw up a comprehensive list of garden features, a sort of checklist. In this way you can decide what you really require and also whether your ideas will fit in with the constraints of the site.

Your checklist might include the following features, all of which will undoubtedly vary in their importance among individuals, as tastes and requirements will differ.

> **TIP**
>
> When drawing up your checklist, remember to be practical and always bear in mind the final plan or design will need to be efficiently maintained. What might look good on paper may turn out to be a problem in its maintenance.

Garden Planning – Checklist (tick as required)

Item/Feature	Essential	Desired	Non-essential
Barbecue area			
Borders			
Bulbs			
Climbing plants			
Clothes drying area			
Compost heap area			
Flower beds			
Fruit plot			
Greenhouse			
Hedges			
Herb garden			
Lawns			
Level changes (steps)			
Patio areas			
Pergola			
Rock garden (or rockery)			
Sandpit (play area)			
Shrubs			
Trees			
Trellis			
Vegetable plot			
Water (ponds)			

This list is only intended as a guide; many more examples could be added.

The Site

Probably the major limiting factor in your design will be the site itself. Many other factors such as drainage, soil type and levels can all be easily dealt with in one way or another, but you can rarely, if ever, change or alter site location and its boundaries.

Garden sites come in all shapes and sizes. Here are some of the sites you may be faced with:

1. Long narrow (rectangular)
2. Corner
3. Triangular
4. Square
5. Circular
6. A site which is totally irregular and may have a combination of shapes 1 to 5 within it.

All of these sites can be improved using basic design principles. For example, the long narrow site should be designed and planted to give the feeling of width; in this way you are trying to lose its long and narrow appearance.

The precise situations of the house and associated permanent buildings will be a major consideration of the site. Their positions will dictate the size of the front and rear gardens and whether or not there are any side gardens or connecting pathways. Very often you will find the garden is bigger at the rear of the house.

Unless the front and rear gardens are suitably connected, it is very difficult to design just one garden. Two designs are often required, using the house as a dividing line between them. This gives a chance to design and build two totally unrelated gardens, and by so doing to enhance the interest of the site.

All garden designs, and in many respects landscape designs, are actually governed by geometric shapes and buildings; the designer has to tailor his designs around these limitations. Designing gardens or landscapes requires a good deal of expertise and planning. Design and planning procedures should follow careful steps and guidelines which should be set out right from the outset, for only in this way will you produce a successful design.

Square

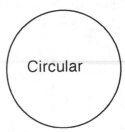

Circular

Rectangle

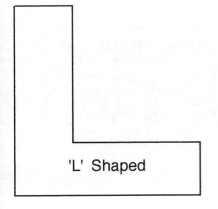

'L' Shaped

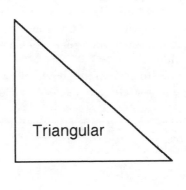

Triangular

Corner

The Design Procedure

Using Existing Plants and Features

Very often it is possible to make use of existing plants and certain garden features in your new design.

Existing plants, such as large mature trees, may provide you with the backbone of your design. Provided the trees are healthy and correctly sited, your design can be tailored around them. Existing features, such as mounds, lawns, shrubs or rock gardens, could be easily adapted into the design. The age, shape and size of shrubs can prove to be very useful and help to give the design a head start in maturity.

! !   **REMEMBER**

Existing large trees may be
protected by Tree Preservation
Orders (TPOs). You need to check
this.

Modifying existing designs requires as much imagination and skill as does designing a garden from scratch. You will probably find you have as many, if not more, constraints in which to work.

     TIP

The construction and planting of
gardens can be costly; if you can
incorporate existing plants or
features you will save money.

Disguising and screening techniques are very useful aids in modifying existing gardens and landscapes. Ugly fences, walls and outbuildings can be effectively screened using vigorous climbing plants such as *Clematis* or honeysuckle. Training climbing plants to grow over permanent outbuildings is a very satisfactory way of screening them and yet at the same time enhancing the appearance of the garden.

However, in some cases you may have to bow to the inevitable; trees or shrubs may well be dead or dying and therefore for safety and disease reasons they should be removed.

Occasionally a dead tree can be used as a support for numerous climbing plants, but make sure it has a reasonably sound structure.

△   **SAFETY**

Examine dead trees carefully before
deciding to keep them as a garden
feature.
Do not use dead elms for this
purpose.

The Basic Principles of Design

The following procedures are suggested as a guide to initial design and planning. These procedures can be adopted for garden design or landscape design. They are:

1. Site proposals
2. Limiting factors
3. Initial designs
4. Final designs
5. Construction details.

Site Proposals

As the designer you will need to know exactly what is proposed for the site, and you must be clear about the aims, objectives and budget allowance. At this stage some indication of the eventual maintenance programme and costings can also be discussed with the client. The discussions about site proposals between the designer and the client should be thorough and detailed, for each should know where they stand right from the outset.

 TIP

Draw up a document about the site proposals as soon as possible, and use it as a term of reference for the design.

Limiting Factors

In order to identify a site's limiting factors, the site needs to be carefully and thoroughly examined; such an examination is often known as an 'analysis'. If the analysis is carried out correctly, all the limiting site factors should be listed. These factors are of great use and importance to the designer, and are needed long before you go to the drawing board. Here are some of the things a site analysis will tell you:

1. Location of access points, existing footpaths and car parks. Planning proposals for the area.
2. Climate: identification of annual rainfall, direction of prevailing wind, exposure, frost pockets and even pollution problems.
3. Soils: identification of soil types, depths, fertility, acidic or alkaline nature.
4. Drainage: the site's drainage ability, existing drainage schemes or badly drained areas.
5. Identification of a site's vegetation: natural vegetation, existing trees and their general condition.
6. Existing site use: existing use of the area, services (if any) to the site, its past history.

Initial Designs

Your first objective is to measure and make an accurate drawing of the existing site. Having found the site's limiting factors, you can now think about design. However, make sure you have carefully examined all the information you obtained from your analysis. An easy way to do this is to draw up a site summary based on your analysis findings, as follows:

Site summary – A checklist
1. Check on planning permissions and any development projects.
2. Check out if there are any Tree Preservation Orders (TPOs) on existing trees.
3. Check the site's soil, making the necessary pH and associated tests.
4. Check the site's access points.
5. Check the annual rainfall for the area and the direction of the prevailing wind.
6. Check that the site does not suffer from any pollution problems. Is the site near to any industrial or large buildings?
7. Check the site for natural or enforced frost pockets.
8. Check on the site's aspect: is it sunny, shaded or exposed?
9. Check the site's drainage potential.
10. Check out the site's existing vegetation.
11. Check the site's 'services' capabilities, for example, gas, electric, water.
12. Check out possible liabilities on the site, for example dangerous trees or waterways.
13. Check on the good features of the site, for example viewpoints.

Using the checklist as a guide you will be able to produce a good site analysis appraisal which will be invaluable when you are preparing the initial designs. In practice, you will find that you are constantly referring to your checklist summary for help and guidance.

At this stage, your initial designs should be a series of sketch plans, incorporating different ideas for the site.

> **! ! REMEMBER**
>
> In your initial designs, particularly those concerned with landscape areas, you need to be sympathetic to the surrounding area(s). The last thing you want to do is to produce a design that is totally out of character with the site and area in which it is situated.

Hard landscape – patio

Final Designs

Once you have done a series of initial designs and you have decided on the one you think will suit the site best, you can begin to transform the design into its final form. When designing sites or landscapes for clients, you should always involve the clients throughout the design procedure. Their input is just as important as the information you acquired through the site analysis.

Initially, you may produce several options on the final design but eventually you must decide on one final design. This design will then be presented in its final and perfected form; it should also show a great deal of detail, such as plant names, surfaces and materials.

Producing the final plan – the key to success
We do not need to be artists or scientists to be able to adequately produce a final plan, however it is helpful if a person has some flair in plan drawing. Most of us can produce successful plans if we follow the principles already outlined, but we need also to incorporate in the design or at least be aware of the following:

1. Scale
2. Balance
3. Rhythm
4. Proportion
5. Unity
6. Colour
7. Textures
8. Shape.

These considerations will play a key role in the success of your final design, and adequate thought and consideration will need to be given to them.

✳ FOR INTEREST

Designing landscapes is often considered as being a combination of Art and Science.

‼ REMEMBER

Today the costs of design, construction and maintenance are high. Your final plan, although it may be visually effective, must also be functional and above all practicable, and particularly maintainable.

When drawing up your final plan, you should ideally aim at trying to integrate all your design features. A designer's ability to produce a final plan with everything in place will be well tested at this stage.

Design Principles

(1) Scale

Most of us are familiar with what is meant by scale – the judgement of features or single elements of the design in relation to the whole of the site. For a garden, scale means making sure that the materials you use in your design for the site are neither too big nor too small for it.

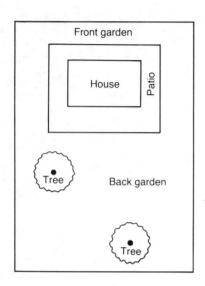

Features in scale

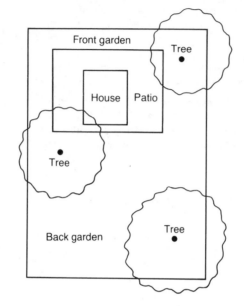

Features not in scale

(2) Balance

Balance is very important to the look and visual effect of the design. The correct use of colour in a garden is an example of balance; vivid colours in one part of the garden can be successfully balanced by green foliage colours in another part. Balance, therefore, does not just mean symmetry, although this is a very good example. There are many ways in which balance can be used or misused in design. The following diagrams show examples of correct use and incorrect use.

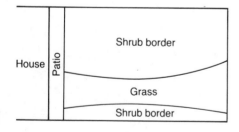

Garden that lacks balance

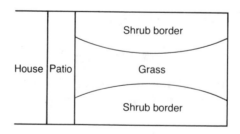

Correct balance

(3) Rhythm

Rhythm is very closely related to unity. It is a way in which we can successfully repeat any design features or elements we may have used – for example, the repetition of curves, shrubs, trees or hard landscape materials. Rhythm, if used correctly, can enhance the design, making it more attractive, varied and pleasing to the eye. Through the principle of rhythm, the designer can effectively make use of shapes, textures, colours, curves or even straight lines – for example, an avenue of trees. Examples of the correct and incorrect use of rhythm are shown in the following diagrams.

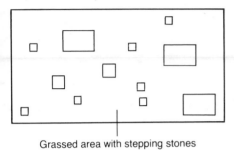

Grassed area with stepping stones

Incorrect rhythm

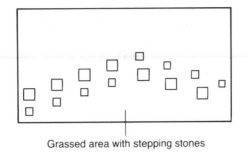

Grassed area with stepping stones

Correct rhythm

(4) Proportion

We are all familiar with the phrase 'keeping things in proportion', and this can be equally employed in Garden and Lanscape Design. Proportion refers to the relative size and shape of features and elements within the design. Features need to be in proportion not only to each other but to the whole of the design. When planting or constructing features, a careful eye should be kept on proportion; the whole design could fail if not enough consideration is given to this. The following diagrams illustrate correct and incorrect proportion.

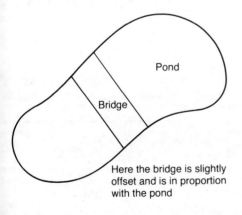

Here the bridge is slightly offset and is in proportion with the pond

Correct proportion

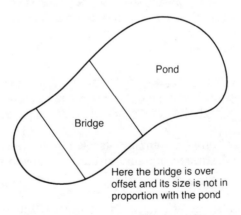

Here the bridge is over offset and its size is not in proportion with the pond

Incorrect proportion

(5) *Unity*

Unity is often associated with harmony, for example in 'the harmony of design'. The whole of the design should be a unified composition, blending together in harmony all the design features and elements. Unity can help the designer link features in all sorts of ways, for example, by grass, roads, paths, water, patios and so on.

However, unity can easily be overdone, and care must be taken to make sure this does not happen. It would be very easy in a large garden or landscape design to over-use plants of different genera. Remember, try to be sympathetic to your natural surroundings, not least of which with the sites adjacent to yours. The following diagrams present examples of correct and incorrect unity.

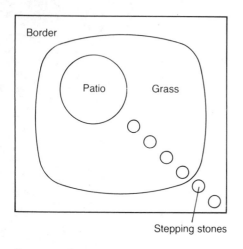

Correct use of unity

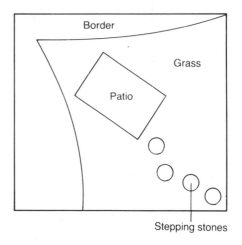

Incorrect unity

(6) *Colour*

There is a wide range of plants and materials which can be used to bring colour into the design. Plants provide us with colour from their flowers and foliage, from vivid colours to more pastel shades. Materials such as paving stones, concrete blocks, bricks or even wood are available in a variety of colours. Both plants and materials need to be carefully thought out before they are used in your design.

(7) *Textures*

Once again, both plants and materials bring texture to the design. A plant foliage may have fine or rough textures, some plants' leaves can be smooth and soft to the touch while others might be more coarse in appearance and be abrasive to the touch.

The faces of pavers, bricks or any other hard materials used in the design also present varying degrees of texture, from soft through to coarse or harsh.

(8) *Shape*

This can refer to individual plants, the site itself or features within the design.

 TO DO

Make a list of those plants whose foliage is (a) smooth and (b) coarse. This will give you two different textural groups.

Equipment, Materials and Symbols used in Plan Drawing

While your early designs/sketches can be done on sketch pads or on paper on the desk top, it is advisable to assemble and use the right drawing equipment in preparing your final plan. The following examples of equipment, materials and symbols are given merely as a guide.

(1) *Drawing board*, with parallel motion, A1 or A0 size.
(2) *Scale ruler*. Make sure it has several different scales on it. It is surprising how many times you may wish to alter the scale of the plan.
(3) *Paper*. An adequate supply of good quality paper is needed, and of the appropriate size. Your paper should fit the drawing board. You will also need a good supply of good quality tracing paper.
(4) *Masking tape*. This is needed to stick your paper and subsequently your tracing paper to the drawing board. Masking tape will make sure your paper does not tear when you remove it from the paper and board. Do not be tempted to use proprietary sticky tape, as this could quite easily damage your paper.
(5) *Pencils*. Choose the correct pencils for plan drawing, and use hard pencils in preference to soft ones. You will also need a pencil sharpener and an eraser.
(6) *Stencil and lettering materials*. These are needed to print labels on your plan. There is an extensive range of dry transfer lettering materials available for use with plan drawing.
(7) *Symbols*. There is a wide range of symbols that can be used on your plan to represent a whole variety of plants and features. For example, the symbols shown in the diagram are used to represent trees in a design.

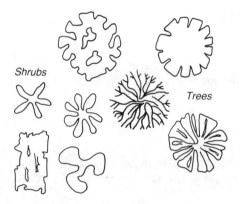

Tree and shrub symbols used in plan drawing

(8) *Drawing pens*. These are special pens specifically for the drawing of plans. It is useful to have a range of these pens, which will mean you have a variety of nib sizes from which to choose.
(9) *T-square and French curves*. These items are useful when drawing straight lines, curves and shapes in your design.

Establishing Amenity Areas

Now that the final designs have been drawn and accepted by the client, the next phase of the work can begin. We need to put the design into practice, a transformation that is not without its problems. The design construction will be in most cases a combination of hard and soft landscaping. Hard landscaping refers to materials other than plants, such as pavers, bricks, wood, fencing and stone. Soft landscaping refers to the use of all plant material from small alpines up to trees and shrubs. To make sure the design will be constructed to a good standard and that the finished product will remain within the budget allowance you have been given, a design specification of works should be drawn up. This specification will be invaluable to both the client, designer and contractor alike during garden or landscape construction.

What is a specification?

This is a document that itemises all the work that needs to be done to construct the design successfully. The document also states (for the benefit of the contractor) exactly how each part of the construction works should be done and to what standard. For example, the designer may have stated that certain works should be carried out to 'British Standards' (BS), whereupon the contractor would have to follow the documentation produced by the British Standards Institution for the relevant works given. For example, in 'specification for planting a standard tree' the designer could specify to the contractor that British Standards should be employed, or the designer could produce his/her own specification. In either event, some of the following would be included:

1. Type of tree, such as bush, standard, heavy standard, etc.
2. Bare rooted or containerised.
3. Depth of planting.
4. Planting composts to be incorporated into the backfill soil.
5. Planting fertilisers.
6. Staking – type of stake, size, diameter, treated or non-treated.
7. Tree ties – type, size, how many per tree, where sited on tree.
8. Pruning – before planting, prune back damaged roots, top growth, etc.
9. Base clearance – that is, weed control, etc.

Specifications, Tenders and Bills of Quantities

Specifications

Specifications can take some time to draw up but they are vital to the construction of the design. Specifications are also extremely helpful in costing the construction works; the appointed contractor can only give the client a realistic price for construction by studying the Specification Documents.

The modern practice for Garden and Landscape Design Construction is for a client to put the works out to 'tender'.

The Tender

Basically, a 'tender' is an invitation sent to contractors telling them that work will be available and inviting them, if interested, to put in a price (tender) for the construction works. Generally speaking, a client would expect to receive several tenders, which can then be looked at individually and a decision made on the one that will win the contract.

Along with the tender documents, a client can also ask potential contractors to provide information about their companies – for example banking facilities, references, similar projects, qualifications and training.

Such a procedure can save time and avoid problems during the execution of the works at a later date. Also, both parties (client and contractor) know where they stand and a suitable contract confirming the Pricing and Schedule of Works can be agreed and signed accordingly.

 FOR INTEREST

It is not always the lowest tender that will win the contract. For various reasons, the client may choose to appoint contractors who have put in higher bids.

Bill of Quantities

A Bill of Quantities is also a necessary document and should accompany the Specification document. The Bill of Quantities helps itemise and cost the entire design. It should:

(a) List the amounts of the different materials and items.
(b) Price each individual item or material.
(c) Be produced in a logical order relative to the execution of works.
(d) Match both the Design and Specification Documents. For example:

Number   Description   Unit   Price   Quantity   £ : p

KIRKLEY HALL LIBRARY

Construction

Professional construction should mean that the site on completion will bear more than a strong likeness to the final design. It should also mean that the features on site are able to establish themselves more quickly without being hindered by poor quality workmanship.

Some Terminology/Definitions used in Landscape Construction

1. *Site clearance*: this should include the removal of long grass, weeds, combustible debris, surface debris and generally any rubbish on the site. All such materials may or may not be burned on site (according to the Specification).
2. *Groundwork*: this refers to excavations, contouring, grading and filling, all such work being associated with the top-soil and sub-soil of the site. In the early development stages of a site, temporary spoil heaps are made.
3. *Fencing*: the erection of barriers either to enclose the site or to mark site boundaries. Various materials, such as wood or wire/plastic, can be used for fencing. Temporary safety fencing might also be needed while construction work is going on – for example, to keep people and animals out of potentially dangerous areas.
4. *Drainage*: the laying of pipes or soakaways for the removal of surface water from the site. Drainage needs to be carried out only after the top-soil has been replaced.
5. *Levelling*: this refers to the measurement of the relative heights or points on the site, pegs being used to show levels. Site levelling is a basic procedure which must be carried out before any construction work begins.
6. *Surveying*: the observation and measurement of the site – for example, measuring the area and the exact positions of boundaries. Surveys are carried out using simple chains and tapes, or technical equipment is used where more accurate surveys are required.

✻ FOR INTEREST

The British Association of Landscape Industries (BALI) keeps a list of professionally registered landscapers. This list could be very useful when you are considering the employment of a contractor.

Tools and Equipment Used in Construction

A variety of tools and equipment is used in the construction of garden and landscape designs. The following is a list of examples, which is by no means complete.

List of Tools and Equipment

Item	Use
1. Spade	Cultivations, planting
2. Fork: garden fork and pitch fork	Cultivations, mulching
3. Rake: garden rake and landscape rake	Cultivations, seed bed preparations, levelling
4. Hoe: Dutch hoe and draw hoe	Cultivations, weeding, drawing drills
5. Trowel	Cultivations, planting
6. Wheelbarrow: various types	Moving materials around the site
7. Gloves: various types	Safety clothing
8. Hammer: various types and sizes	Various
9. Chisels: stone and wood types	Cutting/edging wood or brick
10. Spirit level	Levelling
11. Crow bar	Various
12. Post hole borer	Preparation of fence posts
13. Cement mixer	Mixing cement/concrete
14. Hose pipe	Watering, cleaning
15. Watering can	Watering
16. Wooden pegs	Marking out, levelling
17. Shovel	Cultivations, general
18. Brush: various types	Brushing, tidying
19. Bricklaying trowel	Wall building, pointing, grouting
20. Hedge trimmers	Hedge cutting
21. Rotavators	Cultivations

Hedge trimmers: mechanical hedge trimmers are of great help in the upkeep and maintenance of hedges.

Rotavators: powered pedestrian-operated rotavators are often used in primary cultivations. Many rotavators have the ability to produce fine or coarse tilths, therefore producing the desired seed bed.

You may need to hire some of the tools listed, together with any power tools – for example, a concrete cutter or grinder; make sure you know how to use such equipment properly before you operate it.

We have already discussed in previous chapters how to plant and therefore establish soft landscape such as trees, shrubs, herbaceous perennials and alpines. We need now to look at some examples of establishing/constructing hard landscapes. The examples I have chosen are as follows:

1. Fences
2. Walls
3. Patios
4. Paths
5. Pergolas.

SAFETY

You will need to make sure you have a good pair of safety boots (steel toe-capped). You should not work on a site without them.

SAFETY

If you are using electric hedge trimmers, always make sure the flex is over your shoulder and behind you. This should stop any danger of the flex being cut inadvertently while you are working.

SAFETY

Rotavators can be dangerous machines to handle. Before using a rotavator, make sure you are trained in its operation.

! !   REMEMBER

For the majority of tools and equipment listed above you will need to have some training in their use. Having practical skills of even very basic equipment, such as a spade, is a fundamental requirement if it is to be used correctly.

SAFETY

Make sure you carry out each construction task safely. Adopt safe working practices at all times.

Establishing Hard Landscapes

1. *Fences*

There are many types of fences available, including the following:

(a) Post and rail
(b) Panel – 'closeboard', 'woven', 'wavy edged' and various combinations
(c) Ranch style
(d) Picket
(e) Chestnut and wire
(f) Wire mesh
(g) Plastic
(h) Trellis
(i) Concrete.

Your fence should suit the garden or landscape, and ought not to look out of place. Although fences may be considered as primarily functional, they can also look decorative if the right type is used in the right situation. Most fences are of the timber type and will therefore need regular maintenance; to begin with, choose fencing that has undergone initial wood preserving treatments. An advantage of concrete post/panels and plastic-coated wire is that no such treatments are necessary.

A guide to erecting fencing

1. Mark out the area and put down a line from point A to point B. This will tell you where the beginning and end of the fencing are.
2. Lay out the posts and panels along the line, at suitable intervals.
3. Take out the first hole at the beginning of the line (point A). The depth of the hole will depend on the height of the fence. For example, a post 1.8 m high will need to have about a 75 cm depth. The width of the hole should be as narrow as possible.
4. Before inserting the post, backfill with a little hardcore. Then position the post and backfill with concrete.

   Check that the first post is vertical by using a spirit level. Before taking out the next post hole, measure exactly where it should be by laying out then measuring one of your fencing panels. Check the height of all posts with a straight edge and a spirit level.
5. Place a panel between the posts and fix it into position, with fencing brackets and galvanised nails. Keep the bottom of the panel just above soil level.
6. Support the fence until the concrete sets, using a series of temporary wooden supports along the fence.

 TIP

Posts can be fitted with metal legs. This will ensure that no rotting occurs at the base. However, such posts are expensive.

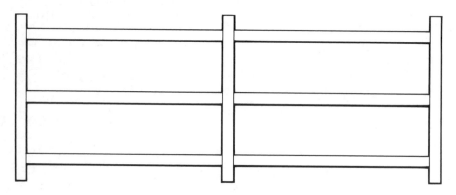

Fencing – 'Post and Rail'

2. *Walls*

Walls can be large or small, depending on what they are used for, but all walls go through various stages during their construction. The following construction stages can be used as a guide:

1. Preparing the foundations
   (a) Mark out area.
   (b) Excavate to the required width and depth.
   (c) Cover base with hardcore and then infill with concrete (mixed on site or delivered).
   (d) Some foundations may need to be stepped.
2. Ordering and selection of materials
   (a) Calculate the length and width of the wall and then assess the number of bricks, blocks or pieces of stone you require.
   (b) Select your wall material, for example, brick, block or stone.
   (c) Have all your materials delivered to the site, including sand and cement ready for your mortar mix.
3. Construction (brickwall)
   (a) Foundations need to be level and of the correct dimensions.
   (b) Beginning at a corner (point A), stretch out a line to point B at the end of the line. Lay a bed of mortar, approximately 16 mm, on the foundation bed. Lay the first brick onto the mortar, then raise the line to the height of the newly laid brick. The line will need to be raised at both ends, and kept tight and straight.
   (c) Check that brick(s) are level, using a spirit level.
   (d) The mortar gap between each brick should be approximately 12–15 mm.

When building a brick wall, various types of bonding can be used. (Bonding is a method of strengthening.)

When preparing the mortar/pointing material, make sure you achieve the correct mix. A mixture of one part cement to three parts of soft/building sand is suitable for most brickwork.

 TO DO

Find out what type of bonding is used for brick walls. Make a list, complete with diagrams.

 TIP

When mixing your materials, it is best to mix the sand and cement dry before adding water. This should ensure you achieve a good, thorough mix.

3 Patios

Patios can be constructed in a range of hard surface materials; they can also be arranged in various shapes and sizes.

If the patio is a component part of a garden or landscape design, you will first need to locate the patio on the site, according to the plan. Once this has been done, you then need to follow a series of guidelines which will help you lay the patio. These are:

1. Remove surface debris.
2. Excavate to the required depth and width. This will depend on what you are using to make the patio. For example, if the patio was to be constructed from concrete blocks (similar to bricks) you would,
   (a) take out enough soil to the depth of the block (about 60/70 mm)
   (b) take out a further 75 mm in lieu of a suitable hardcore material
   (c) take out a further 40/50 mm for a mortar layer.
   In total, your excavations for a patio made of concrete blocks would be about 200 mm.
3. Backfill with hardcore up to 75 mm and consolidate.
4. Place on top of the hardcore a 50 mm layer of dry mortar mix.
5. Lay concrete blocks. Check levels using a straight edge and a spirit level.
6. Brush a mix of dry mortar in between the concrete block joints.
7. Sprinkle water over the entire surface of the patio. This will fuse with the dry mortar mix and set the joints.
8. Clean the entire patio at the finish of operations.

Patio examples: Patios can be successfully constructed from the following materials:

(a) Concrete blocks, known as block paving – various colours and shapes are available.
(b) Concrete paving slabs – various colours, sizes and shapes are available. They are also available in numerous textural finishes.
(c) Crazy paving – broken concrete paving slabs arranged to produce an attractive groundwork pattern. They are laid so as to leave joints which are filled with mortar.
(d) Bricks – hard engineering type bricks can be used in a similar manner to those used for block paving.

4. *Paths*

Paths can be successfully constructed using the same type of materials that are used for patios. The principles of path construction are also similar in this respect. When constructing paths, care must be taken and consideration given to path edgings. Path edgings are of great significance and importance if the path is to be functional.

Decide how long and how wide the path is to be, and what material you are going to use in its construction.

Excavate as necessary, not forgetting the path edgings. These edgings come in various shapes, sizes and thicknesses; you will need to take this into account. Remember also that edgings need to be laid on similar, if not greater, foundations to those used for your path.

5. *Pergolas*

Pergolas can make very interesting features in a garden: they can be used in their own right as a type of free-standing arch or in association with climbing plants. This latter use can be very effective once the plants have had time to grow and establish themselves. Depending on the size of the pergola, you may be able to use more than one type of climber; however, be careful in your selection as numerous climbers have the potential to overrun the pergola, at the expense of other plants.

Before erecting your pergola, you need to decide what material you will use; this simply comes down to a choice of either rustic or sawn wood. In terms of economics, the rustic material should be cheaper. However, for overall appearance, sawn wood (treated) will usually look a little better. The posts of pergolas are erected in a similar way to fence posts; make sure they are secured and straight, and generally follow the guidelines for constructing fence posts. The horizontal beams can either be nailed or notched on, according to your preferences.

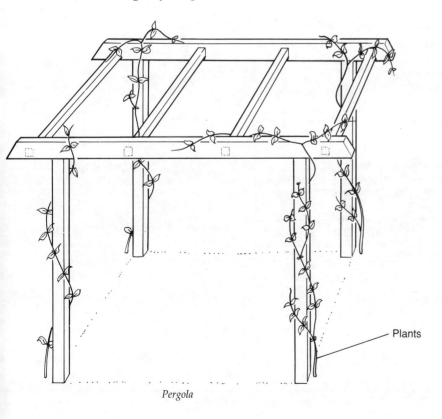

Plants

Pergola

Maintenance of Hard and Soft Landscapes

The Time Factor

After initial construction, all gardens and landscapes will need a certain amount of time to first become established and then to develop. The time taken for a garden or landscape to look how the designer intended may be several weeks, six months, a year or several years. During planting, it is always wise to use a mixture of young, intermediate and old plants, of various heights. In practical and aesthetic terms, this policy means that you will have built a time-factor (the development time) into your design. It also means that the plants will grow and mature at different times, which adds more interest to the garden. It is possible to construct an instant garden using semi-mature trees and shrubs and associated plants, however the governing factor here is the cost of carrying out such works.

Designing for Maintenance

Whether your designs are predominantly hard landscape or soft landscape or a combination of the two, try and design with maintenance in mind. Herbicides are of great help in maintaining landscapes provided the basic rules on selection and application are observed.

Herbicides can achieve low-cost maintenance, especially for tree and shrub plantings where weed control is an important aid to establishment. Many amenity plantings are concerned with woody plants, most of which are tolerant of residual herbicides. Herbicides will effectively reduce competition for light and also the likelihood of reservoirs for pests and diseases.

To achieve good results from residual herbicide applications, you should adopt a code of practice, such as:

1. All planting should be carried out in clean ground.
2. After planting, apply the residual herbicide to a weed-free, moist soil.
3. It may become necessary to 'spot treat' resistant weeds with other appropriate herbicides from the systemic group.
4. Completely eliminate all soil cultivations such as hoeing or forking.

 SAFETY

Handling pesticides is potentially hazardous; make sure you have had training before handling and applying pesticides. Follow the guidelines set down by FEPA.

✱ **FOR INTEREST**

A residual herbicide, when applied to the soil, seals the top 50 mm and prevents weed seed germination. Systemic, means the chemical is absorbed into the plant's system irrespective of where the actual chemical contact has been made on the plant.

Maintenance of Soft Landscapes

As you have seen in previous chapters, a whole range of plants from bedding plants through to trees makes up soft landscapes. Their maintenance will therefore vary. To help in assessing maintenance programmes and time allowances, we can look at maintenance under different headings. These are:

1. Weekly maintenance, for example, grass cutting on ornamental lawns during the summer, or dead heading bedding plants or roses.
2. Monthly maintenance, for example, trimming carpet bedding in summer or weeding borders.
3. Seasonal maintenance, for example, the removal of old bedding schemes prior to the planting of new ones; pruning various trees and shrubs at certain times of the year; various turf operations.
4. Annual maintenance, for example, pruning various trees and shrubs; weed control of borders using pesticides.

 SAFETY

When carrying out all maintenance tasks, both on and off the ground, make sure you use a safe system of working and that you have had proper training in the maintenance skills of each task. For example, the use of chainsaws when pruning trees.

 TO DO

Using the headings in 1–4 above, make up your own list of maintenance tasks associated with soft landscapes.

Maintenance tasks for soft landscapes are extremely varied, ranging from hand weeding and watering through to the more skilful work of pruning. Hedges are a good example: they can be pruned correctly or incorrectly. What time of year should we prune them, how many times a year do we prune and what equipment should we use? These questions can be easily answered provided you know what plants have been used for the hedge.

Hedge Pruning (Clipping)

Approach the pruning or clipping of a hedge in a systematic manner. The following guide will help you:

1. Make sure you have a safe site (adopt safe working practices).
2. Select appropriate tools and method for pruning.
3. Remove clippings and debris from the site.

 TO DO

Find out when you would clip the following hedges:
X Cupressocyparis 'Leylandii'
Fagus sylvatica
Ligustrum ovalifolium
Ilex aquifolium.

Pest and Disease Control

Soft landscapes are vulnerable to attack from a wide variety of pests and diseases – soft fleshy plants being particularly susceptible. To control pests and diseases successfully, a programme of chemical and cultural control should form a part of maintenance work.

Chemical Control

Insecticides and fungicides are one way to control pests and diseases, but if they are to be effective they must be applied at the right time. In the case of insect pests, little control is achieved if the pest is allowed to build up into an infestation before any chemical action is taken. You need to think positively and try to be one step ahead of pests and diseases. Employ the principle that 'prevention is better than cure'; apply pesticides before insects or fungal diseases have had time to build up.

Staking and Tying

A number of plants will initially need to be staked and tied, for example, standard tree planting. Throughout the year it is advisable to carry out regular checks on both the stake and the tie. In the case of the stake, check that it is still firm and secure and in good repair. Check ties for tightness and, if loose, alter as appropriate. Where herbaceous perennials have been used, some may require staking and tying at various times during the growing season; this is often the case with tall-growing species such as *Delphiniums*.

Fertilisers and Mulches

Fertilisers should be added to border plants, trees and shrubs throughout the season as appropriate. Granulated, compound fertilisers are often used; they are easy to handle and apply. Certain plants may well exhibit deficiency symptoms, usually associated with lack of minor nutrients. Generally such deficiencies can be cured using foliar fertilisers giving the deficient nutrient only.

Various bulky organic manures (mulches) can be applied to the soil surface around the bases of plants in early summer. Mulches applied in this way can give good weed control.

Maintenance of Hard Landscapes

As we have seen, hard landscape comes in a variety of materials and can be used for a variety of reasons, not least of which are functional and practical considerations. Patios, in particular, represent a good example of hard landscape, and once they have been constructed they too need to be adequately maintained. Brick walls, fences, raised beds and pergolas will all need maintenance in the years after construction. Here are some of the main hard landscape features used in Garden and Landscape Design, together with a guide to their maintenance.

1. Patio:
   (a) periodically inspect and record any defects
   (b) remove paver, brick or crazy paving as appropriate and
   (c) firstly clean the area and remove debris
   (d) repair as appropriate using the same material as the original and restore to the original design specification
   (e) employ safe working practices and follow the necessary manufacturer's instructions.

2. Walls:
   (a) periodically inspect and record any defects
   (b) clean the area and remove debris
   (c) repair as appropriate – pointing is often required on walls
   (d) employ safe working practices.

3. Fences:
   (a) periodically inspect and record any defects
   (b) repair as appropriate – use the same material as the original and work to the original design specification
   (c) apply wood preservatives at regular intervals
   (d) employ safe working practices.

4. Raised beds:
   (a) periodically inspect and record any defects
   (b) follow the guidance given for 'Walls'.

4. Pergolas:
   (a) periodically inspect and record any defects
   (b) repair as appropriate using the same material and to the same specifications of the original design
   (c) apply wood preservatives at regular intervals
   (d) employ safe working practices

Hard Surfaces

Hard surfaces which are used for patios, paths, drives and steps need to be kept clean. Regular brushing and washing may be needed to meet this objective effectively. Hard surfaces are also vulnerable to moss, lichen or algae invasion, particularly if they are in a shaded area. To avoid a slippery surface, spray with an appropriate and approved fungicide – making sure you follow manufacturer's instructions.

The Cost of Maintenance

I have already mentioned that your designs should always try to balance the functional and practical aspects. Watching the balance will lead to a design that looks impressive yet is practical to maintain. It is very easy to put too much emphasis on the production of your final plans at the expense of maintenance.

Construction costs are classified as *capital costs* (or how much the design costs to build) and *maintenance costs*. The maintenance costs must accordingly be projected.

Maintenance costs will vary, depending on the complexity of the design; very often simpler designs look attractive and need relatively modest maintenance. If turf or grass has been used extensively in the design, grass-cutting labour and machinery will account for a large part of the maintenance costs.

!! REMEMBER

At the end of construction, it is quite likely that your materials would already cost you more if you were to construct the same garden again. What you have to remember is that your maintenance costs will rise each year, as these are future costs.

Contractual Maintenance

Very often, garden and landscape designs, once constructed, are put out to 'maintenance tenders'. Such designs are usually on a large scale and need outside contractual help. Using outside contractors for maintenance work is now an accepted practice, but it can be expensive.

 TIP

If outside maintenance contractors are used, try to appoint contractors who are professionally and adequately trained. Contractors who belong to the British Association of Landscape Industries (BALI) are all screened for their professionalism and competence.

Landscape design

The Consultant's Role to the Landscape Contractor

A professional landscape consultant can be a great help to the landscape contractor, particularly in modern landscape practice. The consultant can give help, guidance and advice on the following:

Dealing with Clients – 'the right approach'

1. Confidence
2. Knowledge
3. Experience
4. Qualifications
5. Professionalism
6. Price
7. The contract

The Work – 'carrying out the job'

1. Interest rates and materials pricing
2. Work to professional standards
3. Is the price right?
4. Work efficiency
5. Client communication
6. Site left clean
7. Client recommendations/information
8. Clerk of Works

The Pitfalls – 'beware problems'

1. Client grievances/disagreements
2. Price variance of works
3. Having no Contract Agreement
4. Bad workmanship
5. Works inexperience
6. Main contracting/sub-contracting
7. Insurance
8. Training
9. Problems

What To Do – 'countering pitfalls'

1. Project/works planning
2. Get the price right - variables?
3. Seek expert advice (re 1 & 2)
4. Legislation/health and safety
5. Litigation/arbitration

6 CROP PLANT PRODUCTION

The UK currently produces and imports a great variety of pot plants and cut flowers, so that the consumer can be offered a non-stop supply. Many of these plants are seasonal, for example, *Cyclamen* (pot plant) is primarily grown for the Christmas market, while others are produced All Year Round (AYR), for example, chrysanthemums (cut flower or pot plant).

Pot plants and cut flowers need to be grown commercially if they are to be viable crops; a range of sophisticated equipment and techniques is used, and nothing is left to chance. Each crop, whether it be a pot plant such as *Azalea* or a cut flower such as carnation, requires its own growing environment and culture. This is one of the reasons why growers generally prefer to grow mono-culture (single) crops, and such growers become specialists in the production of certain types of plants. Although there are growers who do produce numerous crops and grow a wide variety of plants commercially, the area put down to each crop is usually small compared with those used by growers involved in mono-cropping.

Commercial cut flowers

Crop plant production units must work very firmly on commercial lines. The plant's or flower's life is controlled and managed all the way from seed or cuttings to marketing. Each pot plant or individual cut flower has to be produced in the quickest and most cost-effective way to bring in the best price and the biggest return possible.

In Amenity Horticulture, Local Authority Parks Departments and private gardens also produce a large range of pot plants and cut flowers. The destination of these plants is different from those grown commercially. This chapter is concerned with the production and utilisation of pot plants and cut flowers in the Amenity sector.

Pot Plants

Pot plants, or houseplants as they are often called, are those plants which are grown under protective structures, usually heated glasshouses, and used for permanent or semi-permanent decoration in homes, offices, buildings and conservatories.

Before we discuss pot plant types and varieties, we need firstly to examine the production of these plants. In fact they are produced in much the same way as they are commercially, namely, from seed or by some form of vegetative propagation.

For plants raised in Local Authority parks departments or private gardens, seed is often used to propagate flowering pot plants, while cuttings taken from stock plants are often used to propagate the foliage pot plants. As propagation is dealt with in chapter 7, only cultural growing techniques and methods associated with pot plants will be dealt with in this chapter.

Cultural Requirements

(a) *Pots*: you will need to decide what pot or container you are going to use for your plant(s); generally it is a choice between plastic and clay pots. Both are available in a range of sizes and colours, so make sure you choose the one that is best suited to your plant or crop.

(b) *Composts*: like pots, you have basically a choice between loam-based composts (soil based) and loamless composts (usually peat based). The loam-based composts are available as the 'John Innes' series of composts, comprising John Innes numbers 1, 2 and 3 potting composts and John Innes seed compost. Loamless composts are usually based on peat, of which there are various types and grades. They are often used today for the growing of pot plants. When compared with the John Innes series of composts, they are lighter, easier to handle, store better and above all are currently more economic.

(c) *Benching*: make sure the benches used for the accommodation of pot plants are strong enough to take their weight, particularly if a combination of John Innes compost and clay pots is used. The modern approach to glasshouse benching is to use aluminium for bench construction, since this material is stronger than wood and virtually maintenance free.

(d) *Irrigation*: there are many ways in which pot plants can be watered. Here is a short list of examples:
- (i) Using capillary matting*
- (ii) From flat perforated polythene tubing*
- (iii) By trickle or drip irrigation*
- (iv) From overhead spray lines*
- (v) By hand, using a watering can and rose.

An asterisk (*) denotes semi-automatic or automatic systems.

(e) *Feeding*: a number of ways can be used to feed pot plants, for example:
(i) Slow release fertilisers added to the compost. These fertilisers will release nutrients over a period of time in relation to the growth and development of the plant. Such fertilisers are used extensively with composts for pot plants and associated containerised plants.
(ii) Liquid feeds: feeds that are diluted in water and applied to the plant.
(iii) Foliar feeds: feeds that are diluted in water and sprayed onto the plant foliage.

Very often feeds are applied as part of the irrigation, for example, when a plant is watered it is also fed. This is a technique that is often used – it is known as 'liquid feeding'. Liquid feeding on a large scale can be effectively carried out using a 'dilutor'.

 TO DO

Make a list of the advantages and disadvantages of plastic versus clay pots. You may wish to enlist the help of your tutor.

 TO DO

Find out what the ingredients are of John Innes Potting and Seed Composts.

✱ FOR INTEREST

Peat should now be seen as a limited resource for compost use; alternatives are currently being sought. Composted bark, for example, may prove to be a viable alternative.

❗❗ REMEMBER

Choose the irrigation system that will best suit the crop you are to grow.

✱ FOR INTEREST

'Damping down' refers to the application of water to plants and pathways in protective structures as a means of cooling down the plants and their growing environments. It is not a technique/method of watering plants.

 TIP

A hose pipe used correctly offers a very good simple means of irrigation.

 TO DO

Find out which irrigation techniques are used at your college, make a list of their advantages and disadvantages.

 TO DO

Find out how a dilutor works. Your college or your local nursery may have one.

(f) *Staking and tying*: depending on the species, cultivar or variety of pot plant, it may need to be staked and tied.

Staking and tying are carried out on tall pot plants as aids to support, or a series of stakes is used to form a trellis framework, which is especially useful for climbing plants such as *Hederas*.

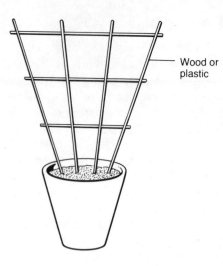

Wood or plastic

Pot and framework suitable for climbing plants

TIP

Where loamless composts are used for large, vigorous houseplants, staking and tying may be inevitable. The compost is quick to dry out, and being light and airy, may not give a tall plant sufficient anchorage. Therefore it is always a good idea to stake and tie such plants before they fall over and become damaged.

(g) *Heating*: for the majority of pot plants, heating is essential if they are to be grown successfully. However, the actual heat requirements do differ according to the species of plant grown. Glasshouse or other protective structures can be heated in a number of ways, for example, by hot water systems, steam systems or warm air systems. Once again, it is a case of selecting the system to suit the crop if this is possible.

(h) *Ventilation*: pot plants require good and adequate ventilation during their growth and development. It is vital that the air within their growing environment is changed regularly; good air circulation will help keep the plants healthy and reduce the likelihood of disease infections. Also, new air brings with it increased supplies of carbon dioxide (CO_2), which the plants can use.

Protective structures can be ventilated in numerous ways. Some examples are:

  (i) Force fan ventilation
 (ii) Ridge ventilation
(iii) Side ventilation

plus combinations of these.

(i) *Relative Humidity (RH)*: is the amount of water that is held in the atmosphere at a given temperature, and is usually expressed as a percentage of the amount which could be held at that temperature.

Many pot plants require high humidity levels during their growth and development – they need the moist temperature created by high humidity levels. Ferns thrive in a moist atmosphere but would do badly in a dry atmosphere. High levels are easily achieved in protective structures; in glasshouses fitted with heating pipes, spraying the pipes with water will create high humidity. Alternatively pathways or benches can be damped down; this method is very useful in the summer months when the inside temperature of a glasshouse can be high.

(j) *Pest and Disease Control*: just like other plants, pot plants are attacked by a wide range of pests which cause various degrees of damage. Pests present a serious problem to pot plants and if not adequately controlled the plants will suffer and could die. Right from the start you should assume your plants will be attacked by pests and act accordingly. If you are growing specific pot plants these are likely to attract specific pests, for example, vine weevil is a problem on *Cyclamen*. Decide what the appropriate control measure is and apply it to the crop. The same procedure can be used against diseases – determine the likely diseases your crop will suffer and decide what the appropriate controls are. A good deal of control can be achieved with pot plants if you adopt a 'prevention is better than cure' strategy.

 TO DO

Make a list of about 20 different pot plants and find out what temperature is best for each plant. What type of heating system would provide these temperatures particularly through the winter months?

! !   REMEMBER

Plants take in and use CO_2 and give out oxygen.

! !   REMEMBER

Not all pot plants prefer high humidity. You should check whether your crop requires high or low humidity levels.

 TO DO

Make a list of about 12 pot plants, and for each plant find out its own humidity requirements.

△   **SAFETY**

When applying pesticides under protective structures, make sure you follow the safe system of work and wear the correct safety clothing, including a respirator.

(k) *Potting*: there are three different variations of potting, namely

1. Potting off – a plant that is potted into its first pot
2. Potting on – a plant that is potted from a smaller into a larger pot
3. Re-potting – removing the plant from the pot and re-potting it into fresh compost either in the same or a slightly bigger pot.

(l) *Shading*: a technique to reduce solar radiation in glasshouses. Various materials can be used ranging from numerous white-washes to blinds. However, the process of shading will reduce photosynthesis which is not really advantageous to the majority of plants. Solar radiation is the main reason for shading, but other important reasons include:

(1) Temperature reductions
(2) To help provide suitable conditions for shade-loving plants
(3) To help increase the life of flowers
(4) To prevent scorching of tender foliage
(5) To reduce fading (bleaching) of blooms.

(m) *Temperature Regimes*: different plants, whether they are foliage or flowering, do require specific temperature regimes. The four temperature regimes used to help group plants for heating purposes are:

(1) Cold
(2) Cool, 5°–15° C
(3) Semi-tropical, 16°–19° C
(4) Tropical, 20°–23° C+.

TO DO

Select two pot plants that would suit the temperature regimes suggested in (2), (3) and (4).

A Calendar Year of Flowering Pot Plants

(one example for each month)

January : Forced *Azaleas*
February : *Kalanchoe*
March : Cineraria
April : *Calceolaria*
May : *Hydrangea*
June : *Fuchsia*
July : *Pelargonium*
August : *Saintpaulia*
September : Pot chrysanthemums
October : *Solanum*
November : *Cyclamen*
December : Poinsettia

TO DO

Add at least one more example of a flowering pot plant for each month January to December.

Growing Amenity Pot Plants

Because the range of pot plants grown in Amenity Horticulture is so great, I have chosen seven of the best known and most widely grown pot plants:

(a) chrysanthemums (pot)
(b) *Cyclamen persicum*   } Flowering
(c) *Hydrangea hortensis*   pot plants
(d) *Primula obconica*

(e) *Begonia rex*
(f) *Hedera helix*   } Foliage
(g) *Asparagus* ferns   pot plants

(a) Pot chrysanthemums

Pot chrysanthemums

Production guide

Ideally, cuttings should be obtained from a specialist producer; this will mean they are in a healthy, pest-free and disease-free condition.

Alternatively, cuttings can be taken from a grower's own stock plants provided the stock is clean and healthy. Cuttings should be potted four or five to a 13 cm dwarf pot between March and October; in the remaining months pot five to a 13 cm dwarf pot. The rooted cuttings should be potted lightly as you do not want to damage the roots at this stage, but remember to water immediately after potting.

The cuttings need to be potted around the edge of the pot and spaced out according to the number to be potted. An ideal potting compost is John Innes Seed Compost (2:1:1 loam, peat, sand) but instead of adding the seed fertiliser, add the fertilisers appropriate to John Innes Potting Compost No. 2. Alternatively, suitable loamless compost and fertiliser additions can be used. To help control the growth of the plant, suitable dwarfing compounds are applied either to the compost mix, or they are given as a foliar spray. In the growing house, the plants are then given the following treatment:

(1) Day length – depending on the cultivar, 0–3 weeks of long-days prior to short-days.
(2) Stopping – stop 10–11 days after planting; this will lead to the production of breaks.
(3) Watering – keep moist up until 14 days prior to flowering.
(4) Feeding – liquid feeds, (a) summer, 300 ppm nitrogen, 200 ppm potash, (b) winter, 200 ppm nitrogen and 200 ppm potash – at every watering.

✳ FOR INTEREST

Dwarfing compounds are chemicals which regulate the growth of plants.

(b) Cyclamen persicum

Cyclamen

Production guide

There are many varieties of *Cyclamen* falling into different strains, for example, short season strains or long season strains. The short season strains are particularly useful for production as they spend less time in the glasshouse compared with the longer season strains. *Cyclamen* are raised from seed, which can be sown in seed trays (space sown) using either John Innes Seed Compost or a loamless compost. Alternatively, they can be individually sown in Jiffy 7's.

For long season crops, seed is sown in later summer, but for short season crops January/February is ideal; this will mean the crop will flower the same year.

TIP

Make sure you use top-quality seed; inferior seed can be difficult to germinate.

Short Season Crop

The seed should be pre-soaked for 24 hours before sowing, and will require a germination temperature of 18–20° C. If the seed has been sown in trays, prick out at the second leaf stage of the seedling and reject any mis-shapen or pear-shaped corms as these seedlings will not produce a good flowering plant. Germination is erratic and can take up to 8 weeks.

The seedlings can be pricked out into 7 cm pots and grown on in the glasshouse, when they can be potted-on into their final pots towards the end of May. Treat Jiffy 7 seedlings in the same way.

For the final potting, use either a loamless compost or John Innes No. 2. If a loamless compost is used you will need to use a suitable liquid feed, for example, a weekly feed of 200 ppm nitrogen and 150 ppm potassium. Throughout the summer, the crop needs to be kept well ventilated and cool. The crop should flower from early autumn onwards.

! ! REMEMBER

When potting the young plant into the final pot, the corm needs to be potted at the same level as the compost. This will mean that, after watering in, it should stand slightly 'proud' of the compost.

(c) Hydrangea hortensis

Production guide

Hydrangeas are propagated vegetatively by taking cuttings early in the year, ideally from stock plants which have been put into a heated (18° C) glasshouse 4–5 weeks earlier. The cutting can be either nodal or inter-nodal, 75–100 mm in length. As hydrangeas respond to both types of cutting, in practice this enables you to assemble an even batch. Each cutting should have two pairs of leaves, and any other leaves should be trimmed back. Cuttings are rooted in a 50:50 mixture of peat and sand or a mixture of peat and perlite. The rooting environment can be either (1) a mist unit (2–3 weeks to root) or (2) a propagation case (about 4 weeks to root). Both environments are housed in a heated glasshouse. Once rooted, the cuttings are transferred to their final pots, usually 13 cm, using John Innes Potting Compost No. 2 with the following additives:

Pink hydrangeas – no lime, pH 6–6.5
Blue hydrangeas – no lime, pH 4.5–5.00, 1 part
                extra peat, plus aluminium
                sulphate as appropriate.

After potting, in late February to early March, the cuttings are allowed to continue growing in the glasshouse until spring, when they are removed to a cold frame. Once a pot begins to fill with roots, feeding can begin; apply 1:0:1 nitrogen and potash feed regularly. Stop plants once they have settled in their pots, with a second stopping when the side shoots from the first stopping have made two pairs of leaves. This second stopping comes at the end of July. From early autumn, move the plants to either a warm glasshouse or a heated frame. keeping them cool but frost free. Cool as necessary to induce dormancy. In early January raise the temperature to 15.6° C which will bring the plants back into growth. Liquid feed at each watering:

Pinks – 1:1:1 NPK
Blues – $\frac{1}{2}$:0:1 NPK

Flowering takes place from April to June.

Hydrangea

! ! **REMEMBER**

Hydrangeas are prone to lime-induced chlorosis when the compost pH is above 6.5

X **USEFUL TERM**

Stopping The removal of the bud or growing point(s).

(d) Primula obconica

Primula obconica

Production guide

There are many species of *Primula* which can be grown as pot plants, for example *malacoides*, *sinensis*, *kewensis* and *acaulis*, however *obconica* is probably the most important as it can be grown throughout the year, making it an ideal pot or decorative plant. *Primula obconica* has a good range of varieties and colours, in various shades of blue, crimson and pink.

Propagation is by seed, sown in John Innes Seed Compost or loamless compost in standard seed trays. Once sown, cover the tray with glass, although no shading is needed, and keep the temperature at about 15.6° C. To maintain a regular supply, sow at appropriate intervals throughout the year. However, the main sowing should be done in March as this produces a sizeable yield towards the end of the year. After germination, prick out seedlings into their appropriate final pots using a John Innes Potting Compost or a suitable loamless compost. Compost pH is important; aim for a pH of 6.0 as this lessens the chance of deficiency problems. Pot the seedlings and stand them on a well ventilated bench for growing on. The temperature should never become too high – shading and constant cooling are required during summer. During autumn and winter, keep the plants a little dry, as they are then able to cope better with the short days. When the flower heads begin to form, feeding can commence. During spring/summer apply a 3:2:1 NPK liquid fertiliser, reducing this to a 1:1:1 in autumn/winter. Watering will need to be increased during the summer. If the plants are grown in a compost with a high pH, they will show signs of chlorosis; in this case iron sequestrene should be applied.

> **TIP**
>
> The blue varieties are favoured in spring, as they hold their colour for a long time.

(e) Begonia rex

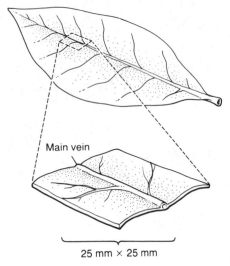

Begonia rex

Main vein

25 mm × 25 mm

Leaf section cutting (Begonia rex)

Production guide

Begonia rex and associated cultivars are good examples of foliage pot plants. They are characterised by their purple, pink, and red/green foliage, and are extremely useful in decorative work or as a single decorative pot plant. Although specifically grown as a foliage plant, they do produce flowers which complement the foliage and as such are a useful bonus. The usual propagation method is vegetative. Two types of cutting can be taken:

(1) Postage stamp cutting – small, 25 mm squares are taken and put into a suitable propagating compost such as 50:50 peat and sand.

(2) Whole leaf cutting – the larger the leaf the better. The leaf is placed on the surface of a prepared tray of propagating compost and pegged down at both ends. This means that the bottom of the leaf is in contact with the compost. If you wish, you may slit the main mid-rib vein of the leaf prior to pegging down, as this should increase the production of callus tissue and so aid rooting. Veins other than the mid-rib are also often cut.

The rooting environment for each type of cutting is a propagation case with soil warming cables to provide bottom heat. Cuttings can be taken throughout the year, but spring/summer gives the best results. Rooting can take a number of weeks, but then cuttings can be potted into 9 cm pots, using loamless compost, lined out on the glasshouse bench and grown on. They will benefit from liquid feeding at regular intervals, once they have settled in the pots. In due course, pot on some of these plants into 13 cm pots, which will give you larger decorative plants.

Keep the plants away from cold spots, draughts and direct sunlight. Do not over-water.

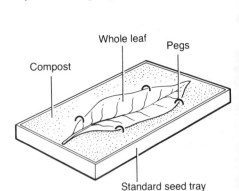

Whole leaf Pegs

Compost

Standard seed tray

Whole leaf cutting (Begonia rex)

 TIP

Do not use a mist unit for the rooting environment, as cuttings tend to die off. The hairy leaves do not like the constant wet atmosphere.

(f) Hedera helix

Hedera

Production guide

Hederas, or ivies as they are commonly called, are now extensively grown as foliage pot plants. They are available in a wide range of cultivars, providing a good colour range. As a pot plant they can be grown in many different situations, for example, in bowls, in hanging containers/baskets or in ordinary containers growing vertically with the aid of a trellis or horizontally.

Propagation is by vegetative means using several types of cutting: (1) nodal, 75–100 mm long or (2) whole leaf and stem segments. Good results can be obtained from both methods.

Use a suitable propagating compost, 50:50 peat/sand suits these cuttings, and plant up a standard seed tray as appropriate. You will produce many more plants using the whole leaf and stem segment method, but they will take longer to develop compared with the conventional nodal cutting. The trays of cuttings should be placed inside a propagation case within the glasshouse. Rooting is fairly quick – in summer only a matter of 2–3 weeks. Cuttings can be taken all year round, but spring and early summer give the best results. Once rooted, cuttings can be individually planted in a suitable loamless compost, using 7 cm or 9 cm pots, and grown on. Alternatively, several cuttings can be potted into a 13 cm pot, complete with trellis, to produce larger and bushier plants. Once they are established in their final pots, a suitable proprietary liquid feed can be used as necessary. Hederas will grow well in conservatory temperatures, and the variegated forms prefer good light conditions.

Hederas make good plants for decoration work. There is no doubt that their popularity has increased over the years, making them a well known and well used group of pot plants.

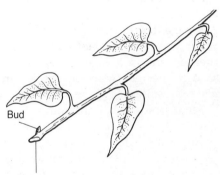

Cut made just below the bud

Nodal stem cutting (Hedera)

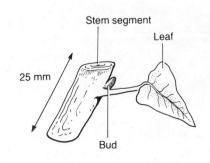

Stem segment

Leaf

25 mm

Bud

Whole leaf and stem segment cutting (Hedera)

(g) Asparagus Ferns

Asparagus fern

Production guide

Asparagus ferns, contrary to their name, are not true ferns as they are propagated by seed, not spores. As pot plants, they are widely grown for their decorative foliage and are used in a variety of decorative situations. Two of the most popular species are *Asparagus sprengerii* and *Asparagus plumosus*, although there are many more species and varieties available.

Seed is usually bought from a specialist producer, to ensure it is of good quality. The seed can be sown throughout the year, which means you can produce these ferns in succession to suit your requirements; however, early spring and late summer are the best sowing times.

Unless large quantities of these ferns are required, they are usually propagated on a small scale in Amenity Horticulture. Seed is sown in 13 cm pots in a compost of pure peat, which can be further sterilised by pouring a little boiling water over the peat. Seed is individually sown to a depth of 6 mm and covered. After sowing, secure the top of each pot with polythene and stand the pots under the glasshouse bench; this will give them the partial shade they require. Maintain a glasshouse air temperature of about 19° C; germination is erratic and can take a number of weeks. Once 75% germination has been achieved, remove the polythene layer. When the seedlings have reached a height of 25 mm they can be pricked out into suitable pots and compost. You can grow the plants as small single plants in 9 cm pots, or by planting 3–5 to a 13 cm pot, you can grow more substantial plants. Once mature they will flower, particularly *Asparagus sprengerii* which produces small white flowers followed by decorative orange berries. Begin liquid feeding with a suitable fertiliser once they are established in their final pots.

✳ FOR INTEREST

Pre-soaking the seed prior to sowing will increase germination.

Cut Flowers

There are a great many different types of cut flower grown commercially in the UK, many of which are produced all year round. Some examples of commercial cut flower crops are:

1. Bulbs – *Narcissus*, Tulips, Lilies, Bulbous Iris
2. Corms – Gladiolus, *Freesia* (*Freesia* can also be grown commercially from seed)
3. Carnations
4. Chrysanthemums
5. Dried flowers
6. *Gerbera*
7. Orchids
8. Roses
9. *Dahlia*
10. Sweet Peas
11. Sweet William.

   Other specialist-grown cut flowers include *Alstroemeria*, *Anemone*, *Ranunculus*, *Gypsophila* and a range of herbaceous flowers.

   In Amenity Horticulture, cut flowers are only grown on a small scale. For example, Local Authority Parks Departments only tend to produce crops that can be grown outdoors and in their natural season. Such crops include Dahlias, Sweet Williams, Sweet Peas and Pinks. Cut flowers in Amenity Horticulture provide a useful back-up to pot plants for decorations at civic and associated functions. Thus they are not required in the same numbers as pot plants. Also, cut flower production is a very skilful and time-consuming task, which is one of the reasons that their production is left to the commercial sector of the industry.

Growing Cut Flowers

As you can see, raising cut flowers requires some degree of specialism with a thorough working knowledge of a crop's individual cultural requirements. Professionally, crops are grown to time; that is, they are planted and harvested at pre-set times – commercially these times being associated with the market place. For example, growing crops out of season or for a specific date such as Easter or Mother's Day will bring in higher monetary returns. This is also practised in the Amenity situation, but for different reasons. There are many problems associated with growing cut flowers, for in addition to their cultural requirements they tend to be vulnerable to a wide range of pests and diseases.

 TO DO

For each of the cut flower crops 1–11, state one potential pest and one potential disease.

Growing Requirements

Whether your crop is grown under glass or outdoors in pre-prepared areas, the soil type and its condition are very important factors. In general terms, cut flowers prefer free-draining soil with a light to medium texture. Soil fertility should not be a problem when growing cut flowers on a small scale, as we can improve the fertility of a soil to suit the crop. This can be done by adding materials such as lime and various manures as appropriate. Liming, together with an application of the required fertilisers, if required should be carried out before the crop is planted.

If the crop is to be grown outdoors, as is generally the case in Amenity Horticulture, make sure you choose a site that can be easily protected and is not likely to suffer excessive frosts. All-year-round crops grown under protective structures will need some heat during the winter period if they are to be grown successfully. As you can see, growing cut flowers outdoors is seasonal, making use of a plant's natural growing season. However, as these plants tend to be fleshy/soft plants, they are vulnerable to cold/frosty weather.

Outdoor cut flower beds of *Dahlia* and chrysanthemums will also need staking, otherwise they could suffer wind damage.

If cut flowers are to be grown constantly, then crop rotation will be needed to offset the build-up of numerous soil-borne diseases and volunteer plants; this also helps with weed control and improves soil fertility. Crop rotation is just as important under glass as it is outdoors.

Cut flowers need suitable irrigation and fertilisers. Very often the crop itself dictates the method of irrigation used and its fertiliser requirement. Watering and fertiliser application is frequently combined, particularly for cut flowers grown under glass, as the plants absorb nutrients in solution. Liquid feeding is therefore most appropriate.

> ### ＊ FOR INTEREST
>
> Volunteer plants are those plants that occasionally grow alongside crop plants. Such plants should be removed and destroyed.

Harvesting Cut Flowers

While some flowers have a long vase life, others wither very quickly. The key to prolonging vase life lies in the harvesting – the timing of the harvesting of a crop or individual stems is both a skilful and important task. Long before harvest, the flower has developed progressively from a tiny bud to a mature flower; it has enjoyed the benefit of being part of a plant, with all its food and water supplied. Harvesting removes individual flowers from the parent plant, so that they lose their food and water supply. So once cut, the flower can quickly die if it does not receive the correct treatment. In general terms, flowers that are handled properly last nearly as long as they would do on the plant. Some of the main factors when dealing with cut flowers are:

(a) *Water* – very important, newly cut flowers must be placed in water quickly. Do not allow their cut ends to dry, as this blocks the fine water-carrying tubes in the stem. If undetected, this blockage causes wilting and shortens the vase life. Use clean uncontaminated water and change the vase water at least weekly.
(b) *Nutrients* – if the flowers are cut when mature, they will have no need for liquid feed solutions.
(c) *Temperature* – try and cool the flowers immediately after harvesting; ideally they should be given a cool moist atmosphere.

> ### ！！ REMEMBER
>
> Do not harvest immature blooms, as they have a very short vase life.

> ### ！！ REMEMBER
>
> High temperatures with low humidity will increase both the respiration and transpiration rates of the flower, which will reduce its vase life.

7 | PLANT PROPAGATION

Methods and Techniques

There are two basic methods of propagating plants:

(a) from seed
(b) by vegetative means.

Both methods are equally important in the raising and production of plants, but vegetative methods require higher degrees of skill. The seed and vegetative techniques are long established and traditional methods of increasing plants. While seed propagation is still a very important method of raising or increasing plants, many of our traditional vegetative techniques are being superseded by new and improved techniques. Today, more than ever, a grower or propagator has to be aware of and be skilful in the wide range of techniques now used for the propagation of plants. The Commercial sector of the industry, through nurserymen and nursery stock producers, propagates and grows on a very wide variety of plants specifically for sale. Garden centres, retail nurseries and chain stores represent some of the large outlets for commercial plant sales. In Amenity Horticulture, plants are propagated not for commercial gain but for some of the following reasons:

(a) the continuation of a species
(b) to have material available for replacement plantings
(c) to produce material for new plantings
(d) for the upkeep of material used in decoration work
(e) aesthetic reasons – growing material simply to look at

Production of plants in Amenity Horticulture therefore is on a much lower scale compared with Commercial Horticulture. However, the skills and expertise required for propagating plants are the same in both sectors, the major difference being in the amounts produced.

This chapter summarises a range of methods and techniques, and gives appropriate practical guidelines for their success.

(a) Seed

Under normal conditions the majority of flowering plants produce seed. Seed production is fundamental to their life cycle and is probably their main functional task. For the Botanist, the seed is the resting stage of the plant. It contains the embryo; this is a tiny new plant which, when given the correct conditions, will germinate and produce a new plant. Seed comes in all shapes and sizes but is divided in Botany into two distinct groups:

1. Monocotyledons – a single seed leaf
2. Dicotyledons – two seed leaves.

Both of these seed groups belong to the order of plants known as the Angiosperms.

Plants produce seed once they have been successfully pollinated and then fertilised. Regarding pollination, 'self-pollination' or 'cross-pollination' methods are used, and in the case of cross-pollination a wide range of climatic elements and insects are involved. Once fertilisation has been successfully achieved, seed will be produced.

 TO DO

Name three examples of monocotyledonous and dicotyledonous plants.

 FOR INTEREST

If you want to know about the botanical aspects of seed production, why not look at a Botanical or Biological Textbook, like Brimble, *Intermediate Botany* (Macmillan)

Raising plants from seed is the easiest and cheapest method, and also efficient and reliable, although there is often variation with seed-raised plants. Seeds are usually easily obtained from numerous seed companies or through retail outlets, and supplies are only halted if for some reason the crop fails to set seed. On a small scale it is possible to collect your own seed, but for this type of collection to be successful you need to know the correct harvesting times and procedures as well as the seed's storage requirements.

TIP

Only collect seed from healthy disease-free stock plants that show vigour and good plant characteristics.

! ! REMEMBER

Some plants cannot be realistically raised from seed, therefore for these plants vegetative methods are used.

Seed Storage

Once seed is harvested it needs the correct storage conditions. Most seeds require one of three types of storage:

(a) Dry storage, with little if any temperature control. This environment is acceptable to many different seed types. The moisture levels in the air will need to be less than 50%. This type of storage is suitable for many of our garden plant species, with a storage life expectancy of up to 3 years or more.

(b) Cool but dry storage. Here the temperature is controlled within the range 2–10° C; this will provide a regime that is above freezing yet cool. Seed viability under this type of storage is reasonably high, giving many years of potential viability.

(c) Cool but moist storage. You will need to provide a similar temperature as in (b), but increase the moisture content of the air (Relative Humidity) by 15–20%, giving about 70% or more as appropriate. This type of storage is suitable for many woody plants, particularly trees and shrubs.

Seed Testing

All seed sold in the UK has to be tested and in addition comply with the rules and regulations as laid down under the Adulteration of Seeds Act (this is an Act of Parliament specifically set out to protect seeds and seed consumers).

Seed Germination Requirements

Once seed has been harvested and successfully stored, the seed, when the time is right, will emerge from its resting stage and, given the right germination conditions, germinate.

The main requirements for seed germination are:

(a) the embryo must be alive – it must be viable;
(b) water (H_2O) – a moist environment;
(c) temperature – an appropriate germination temperature for the seed species must be given;
(d) oxygen – the seed will require airy conditions;
(e) light – this is only a requirement for certain seed types.

As long as the seed is viable, water, temperature and oxygen have a vital role to play in its germination; without them in the appropriate amounts, your seed is likely to remain dormant (resting). In nature, the individual seed is reliant on the elements to provide suitable conditions for germination; however, some seeds contain chemical inhibitors which stop them germinating, even in the right conditions. Cultivated seed that is known to have such inhibitors is chemically treated to eliminate this problem.

Provided all is right for germination, seed will germinate producing a seedling. The appearance of a seedling above soil/compost level is called 'emergence'. Before germination can take place, seed has to take in (imbibe) water, and this in turn triggers off a whole series of reactions within the seed which results in germination. Some seed may take several seasons to germinate. There are numerous reasons for this, for example:

(a) the seed coat may be impervious to water;
(b) the embryo has not developed sufficiently;
(c) not enough exposure to low temperatures has been given;
(d) chemical inhibitors are present;
(e) combinations of the above reasons.

TIP

Green seed is better stored in polythene bags rather than card or paper bags.

TIP

For each type of seed storage: (a), (b), (c), any seeds placed inside suitable containers will keep their viability for a long time.

✳ FOR INTEREST

Seeds need to be at their peak if successful germination is to be achieved. It is for this reason that 'seed testing' is important. Seed of a number of plants is becoming more expensive, particularly seed of the F_1 hybrids; we need to be sure that the seed we sow will have a very high germination rate.

! ! REMEMBER

A seed is the product of a fertilised ovule – a young embryo plant. You must at all times handle seed with care. Undue pressure can cause an increase in its respiration rate and lessen its chances of germination.

Seed Stratification

This technique is used to break the dormancy or rest period of the seed. It is often used on tree and shrub seed and is especially useful in breaking the dormancy of seed inside flesh fruits or berries. Stratification will allow the embryo to develop and grow so that in time germination will follow. The technique is to mix moist sand with the seed or simply place a layer of seed between two thicker layers of sand. Tree and shrub seed which are surrounded by fleshy fruits, for example, *Pyracantha*, *Berberis*, *Sorbus* or *Malus* species, can be stratified in this way. The fruits should be collected when ripe and then stratified in either polythene containers or suitable seed trays. A suitable north-facing orientation is then found in the garden or nursery and a pit is excavated; on a small scale, dimensions of 1 m × 1 m × 0.5 m would be suitable.

TIP

Once you have excavated the pit, surround it entirely, including the top with chicken wire. Seeds stored in this condition make an easy target for rodents looking for food in the winter.

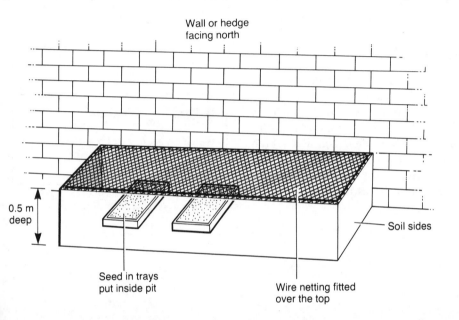

Wall or hedge facing north

0.5 m deep

Soil sides

Seed in trays put inside pit

Wire netting fitted over the top

Seed stratification pit

Seeds in this condition should be left through winter when they should experience the right conditions to break dormancy. Seeds which require only one winter's stratification can be removed from the stratification pit and sown as appropriate. Seeds which require two winters should be left. Seeds can be sown in seed trays, cold frames or outdoors in drills. Germination rates are usually high provided you have selected the right species for this treatment.

Seeds with hard coats, such as *Wisteria*, often have their germination delayed. This problem can be overcome in a variety of ways, for example by using

(a) certain acid treatments
(b) heat treatments
(c) chilling.

✳ FOR INTEREST

Examples of species having periods of stratification from 18 month to 2 year are *Ilex*, *Magnolia* and *Crataegus*.

The Advantages and Disadvantages of Seed Propagation

Advantages:
1. Generally there is freedom from disease.
2. Plants will naturally promote the production of seed.
3. Seed propagation allows us to produce F_1 hybrids.
4. Storage and transportation of seed is easier when compared with vegetative propagation.

Disadvantages:
1. Variation.
2. The climate of the UK is not really suitable for large-scale seed production as we tend not to get enough sunshine hours.
3. Some seed can be difficult to germinate.
4. Some seed can carry disease.

The Production and Advantages of F_1 hybrids

F_1 stands for 'first generation' seed. This is seed which is produced from genetically different parent plants. The hybridisation cross must be performed annually from parent plants which have been maintained in pure breeding conditions. Hybridisation is both an important and a useful technique aimed at improving plants and plant varieties. Today a whole range of F_1 hybrid seed is available, covering a wide collection of plant species. Hybridisation of varieties will produce a 'variety hybrid', hybridisation of species produces a 'species hybrid', and hybridisation of genera produces a 'generic hybrid'.

The advantage of F_1 hybrids are

1. They produce hybrid vigour.
2. They give a greater uniformity of plant.
3. They often produce larger flowers.
4. They are often more disease resistant.
5. They generally have a longer flowering season.
6. They have a greatly improved habit.
7. They promote vegetative propagation and hybrid vigour can be perpetuated indefinitely.

 TO DO

Name an example of a variety hybrid, a species hybrid and a generic hybrid.

Sowing Seed

Various techniques are used in the sowing of seed, the main reason for this being seed size. On a small scale, seed can be sown by hand or from the packet; on a larger scale, seed drilling equipment would be needed, therefore the task becomes mechanised. Knowing your seeds' requirements is crucial to the success of their germination; often an information guide is provided on the back of seed packets.

Seed Beds, Seed Sowing Composts and Seed Depths

Seed beds: seed bed preparation is necessary for any seed that is to be sown outdoors, irrespective of the seed being sown in drills or by broadcasting techniques. Land that is to be used for seed sowing should be prepared well in advance, for example, autumn or winter digging for spring sowings. On a small scale, the soil can be effectively broken down using garden forks and garden rakes. Shuffling over the site on the heels or balls of your feet will help firm the seed bed. Your finished seed bed should reflect the type of seed you are to sow. In general terms, the finer and smaller the seed is, the finer the nature of the seed bed (or the finer the 'tilth', as it is known) should be.

Seed sowing composts: there is a wide variety of seed sowing composts available today, so make sure you choose the compost that best suits your seed's requirements In Amenity Horticulture, a range of loamless seed sowing composts is used, these composts being usually based on peat. Proprietary brands of loamless compost are frequently sold to the Amenity industry, and many do state that they have been mixed specifically for seed sowing. You can, if you wish, mix your own seed sowing compost. Mixing peat with the following materials provides a number of seed compost alternatives:

(a) peat and perlite
(b) peat and vermiculite
(c) peat and sand
(d) peat and polystyrene
(e) peat and any mixture you desire from (a)–(d), for example, peat, perlite and sand.

We can therefore pre-select or mix a compost which will in every way meet the germination requirements of a wide variety of seed types.

Seed Sowing Depths: it is very important to sow seed at the correct depth. When sowing, remember to check the information on the back of the packet.

! ! REMEMBER

You can add various fertilisers to your compost mixes depending on what seed is being sown. This is particularly so if the seedlings are to remain in the seed trays for some time.

(b) Vegetative Propagation

Vegetative propagation is widely practised throughout Horticulture and it is a well known and long established method of propagating plants, using a wide range of techniques. However, man is not solely responsible for propagating plants vegetatively, as plants themselves are quite capable of propagating themselves naturally.

Natural Propagation: Some Examples

(1) Bulbils:
Bulbils are found on *Lilium* species. Once they are formed and ripe they can be eased out of the axil using a finger and thumb. Then they can be potted in a suitable compost and grown on.

(2) Bulbs:
Bulbs are produced naturally by a number of plant species; daffodils, tulips and hyacinths are all good examples. The daughter bulb of a daffodil is simply removed and grown on.

(3) Corms:
The old corm is directly beneath the new corm; *Crocus* is a good example of a plant that produces corms.

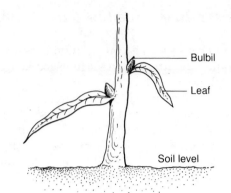

Bulbil (Lilium species)

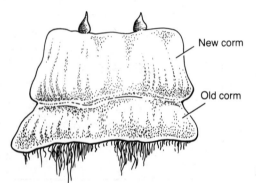

Example of a corm – Crocus

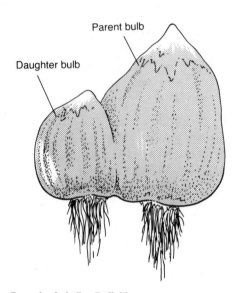

Example of a bulb – Daffodil

(4) Creeping stems:
Ground ivy produces creeping stems which creep just above ground level. Along its length it frequently produces new plants arising from nodes and buds which are sited at intervals along the stem.

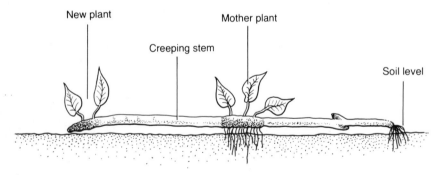

Example of a creeping stem – Ground ivy

(5) Offsets:
Offsets are produced at the base of a parent plant; House Leeks often produce offsets in this way. Offsets should be removed with a knife, potted on and grown on accordingly.

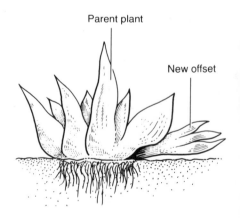

Example of an offset – House leek

(6) Rhizomes:

Rhizomes are a type of underground stem, with numerous segments producing axillary buds. Axillary buds develop into new plants and will in time produce their own rhizome. Many *Iris* species produce rhizomes.

(7) Runners:

The well known strawberry plant produces runners. Runners are growths which grow away from the parent plant horizontally, producing new plants when a suitable bud comes into contact with soil. This contact results in the production of a root system and a new plant.

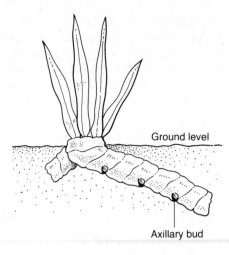

Example of a rhizome – typical Iris species

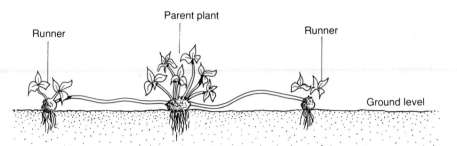

Example of a runner – Strawberry

(8) Stolons:

Wild and cultivated forms of blackberries produce stolons. Stolons are arching branches which are produced by the parent plant and are pushed outwards away from its centre. Where the tip of the stolon meets the soil surface, roots are formed and therefore a new plant is produced.

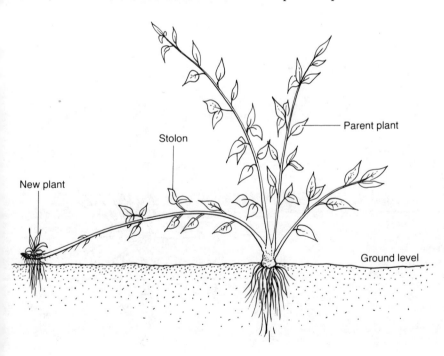

Example of a stolon – Blackberry

(9) Suckers:

Raspberries produce suckers. Each parent plant or cane will produce a type of underground stem giving rise at regular intervals to sucker growths. These suckers in turn will grow and produce their own suckers in due course. On established plants a great deal of suckering can be expected, becoming quickly invasive of surrounding land and plants.

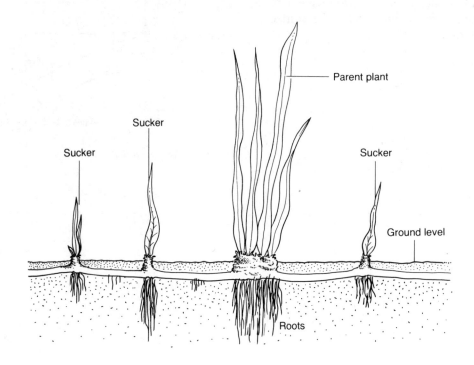

Example of a sucker – Raspberry

(10) Tubers: (a) Stem tuber

Potato is an example of a stem tuber. Stem tubers form as the swollen end of the underground stems.

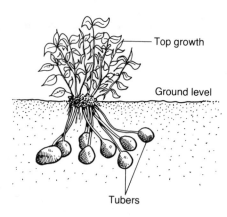

Example of stem tuber – Potato

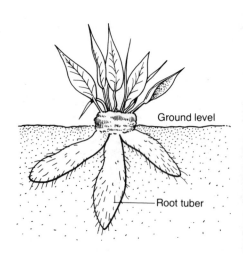

Example of a root tuber – Dahlia

(b) Root tuber

Dahlias are an example of a plant that exhibits root tubers.

Vegetative Propagation Techniques

The vegetative propagation of plants is just as important in Amenity Horticulture as it is in Commercial Horticulture, albeit for different reasons. In Amenity Horticulture, we increase the numbers of plants by a whole range of propagation techniques. There are various reasons why numbers need to be increased:

1. For summer bedding displays, for example, *Pelargonium*.
2. For civic decoration, for example, a range of foliage houseplants.
3. For container user, for example, a range of pot plants or patio plants.
4. To preserve the plant species.

Some of the main techniques used are:
1. Cuttings
2. Layering
3. Grafting
4. T-budding
5. Chip budding
6. Micro-propagation.

TO DO

Name one example of a plant that can be propagated from the techniques listed in 1–6.

TIP

Plant division is also a very good propagation technique, particularly where herbaceous perennials are concerned.

1. Propagation from Cuttings

There are many different ways in which cuttings can be taken, and these involve a wide range of techniques. Such techniques include:

(a) Stem cuttings.
    (i) softwood, (ii) semi-ripe, (iii) hardwood.
(b) Leaf cuttings
    (i) leaf section, (ii) leaf petiole, (iii) leaf bud.
(c) Root cuttings.

When propagating plants vegetatively, decide the appropriate technique for your plant. The correct technique is critical to the successful rooting of the cutting. Use this checklist as a guide when propagating plants from cuttings.

Cuttings Checklist
1. Choose the type of cutting required.
2. Select the type of compost that the cuttings will require. For example, if Ericaceous species are to be taken, you will need to use a suitable peat-based compost as these plants prefer acidic conditions.
3. Decide on the appropriate rooting environment for the cuttings – for example, a mist unit or a cold frame.
4. Choose the right time of year to take the cuttings – this will depend on the individual plant species.
5. Select the appropriate systemic fungicides that the cuttings should be given. One or several fungicidal applications will be needed to help control disease.
6. Decide on the appropriate after-care of your rooted cuttings. For example, do you intend to containerise them or alternatively line them out in the nursery?

(a) *Stem cuttings*

All three types of stem cutting can be propagated by taking (i) nodal, (ii) inter-nodal or (iii) heel cuttings. However, in practice we adopt the following principles:

  (i) softwood cuttings: nodal or inter-nodal, taken in early summer.
 (ii) semi-ripe cuttings: nodal or heel, taken in autumn.
(iii) hardwood cuttings: nodal, taken in the dormant season (winter).

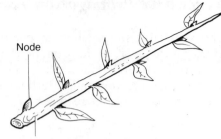

Cut made just below the node

Stem nodal cuttings

(b) *Leaf cuttings*

The three different types of leaf cutting are often used in Amenity Horticulture because they are particularly suitable for houseplants and shrubs.

(i) Leaf section: for example, *Begonia rex* species and *Streptocarpus*.

Alternatively the whole of the *Begonia* leaf can be used as a large leaf cutting in its own right. The leaf would simply be pegged down in the seed tray onto a suitable compost.

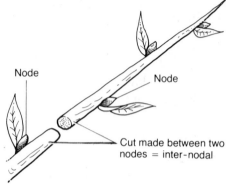

Inter-nodal cuttings

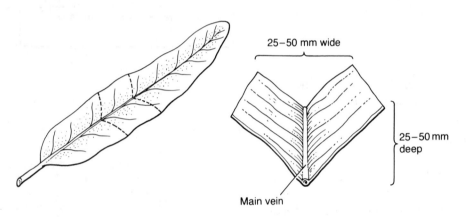

Typical example of a leaf section – Streptocarpus species

The leaf sections of both *Begonia* and *Streptocarpus* are placed in seed trays using an appropriate 'cuttings compost' as follows:

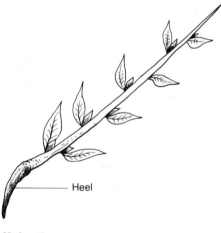

Heel cuttings

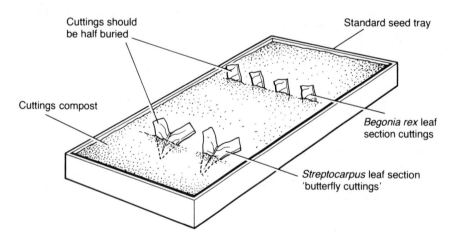

Example of cuttings insertion

The cutting should be placed so that one half of it is below the compost while the other half is above the compost.

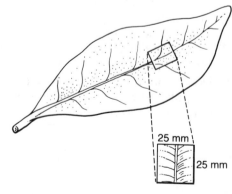

Dealing with leaf section cuttings – Begonia species

(ii) Leaf petiole: for example, the African violet (*Saintpaulia*).

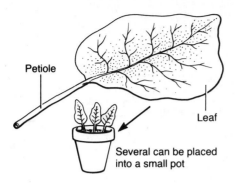

Example of a leaf petiole cutting – African violet

Using a sharp knife, remove an appropriate leaf and keep intact its leaf stalk (petiole) to a length of approximatey 25–25 mm. Place the cutting in either a tray or a pot filled with a 'cuttings compost'.
(iii) Leaf bud: for example, a Rubber plant (*Ficus*).

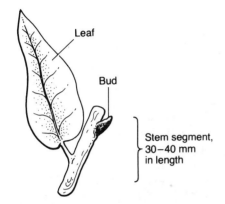

Example of a leaf bud cutting – Rubber plant

Once the cuttings have been taken, place them in trays or pots using a suitable 'cuttings compost'. Plunge the cutting into the compost, leaving the bud to show at surface level.

(c) *Root cuttings*
A number of ornamental plants can be successfully propagated by root cuttings, for example, *Primula denticulata*, *Phlox* species or Sumach (*Rhus typhina*). With these plants, this method makes use of the naturally produced root suckers and turns them into root cuttings.

Plants that are characterised by this type of propagation tend to be difficult, if not impossible, to root by other means. Such information is of great importance to a propagator who wishes to increase stocks of these types of plant.

Remove a segment of root, complete with its eye (or bud), and place it in a prepared tray of compost. The size of the cutting depends on the size of the root and the individual plant species. In general terms, the larger you make the root segment so the more food reserves there will be to sustain the bud for growth and development until the cutting becomes a new plant.

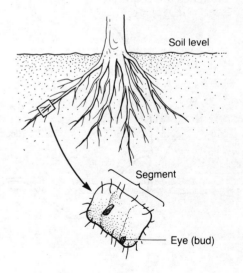

Example of a root cutting – Primula denticulata

143

2. Layering

This old and well established technique can be used for a number of plants. The technique has three variations: (i) simple layering, (ii) serpentine layering and (iii) air layering.

For all three, the actual technique is the same. First make a cut on the stem or branch (known as a lateral) of a plant and, using either moss or a thin piece of wood, wedge it open. Then cover the whole of the cut with soil if you are doing simple or serpentine layering, or with sphagnum moss for air layering.

Simple layering: for example, *Rhododendron* species.

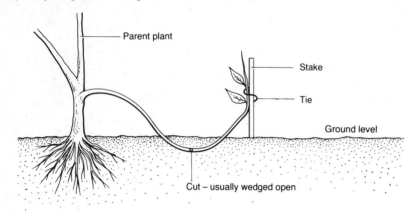

Example of simple layering – Rhododendron

Select your branch, bend it down to the required depth and make the required cut; prepare the hole beforehand. Backfill the hole and tie the end of the branch to a vertical cane; this will ensure that, once you have rooting, you will also have a normal and straight-looking plant. Simple and serpentine layering of Rhododendrons, although effective propagation techniques, are time-consuming as plants can take the best part of a year to root.

Serpentine layering (an extension of simple layering) – (long flexible branches are required).

Serpentine layering

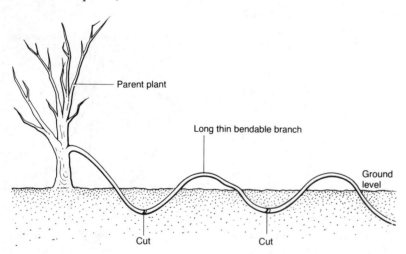

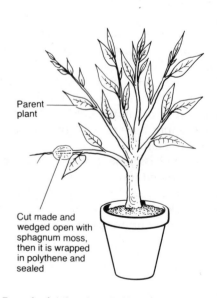

Air layering: for example, the Rubber plant (*Ficus* species).

Place polythene over the layer and tie it at each end. Check periodically for drying out, and unwrap and water if necessary. When you begin to see roots through the polythene, remove the polythene and then the new plant from the parent plant. Pot up in a suitable compost and grow on.

Example of air layering – Rubber plant

144

3. Grafting

Grafting is the technique of joining two parts of different yet genetically compatible plants together. Although grafting has been practised for many years, the technique for the vegetative propagation of plants is still popular and widely used. There are many different types of graft from which to choose, however to make sure of success you should select the appropriate graft for the plants you are dealing with. Grafting is mainly practised in the Commercial sector, being well used in the production of nursery stock. In the Amenity sector, while we may use some grafts in our quest to propagate certain ornamental plants, it is not carried out on a large scale.

The Whip and Tongue Graft

This is an old established and traditional graft, and one that over the years has been associated with top fruit, particularly apples (*Malus*).

Firstly, cut down the stock to within 250 mm of ground level. The stock (rootstock) is prepared by making a cut approximately 25 mm long in the centre of the stock. This cut is not deep; it is just enough to remove the skin layer.

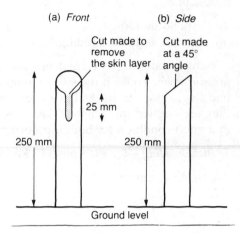

Whip and tongue grafting – initial treatment of stock

A cut is made on the stock by putting the knife in firstly at a 90° angle and then turning the knife to 45°. Start the cut a third of the way from the top of the stock, and finish the cut halfway down the stock's cut surface.

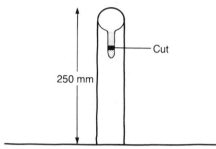

Whip and tongue grafting – secondary treatment of stock

The material you graft onto the stock with is known as the 'scion'. The slit (tongue) is made on the scion using the same principle as for the stock, except that the cut is made in the opposite direction. For ease of handling, scions should be shortened to 3 or 4 buds (100 mm long).

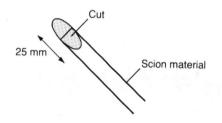

Whip and tongue grafting – preparing the scion

Stock and scion are now ready for fixing together.

Once the graft is in position, it needs to be tied with grafting tape.

On *Malus* species, this graft is carried out in March.

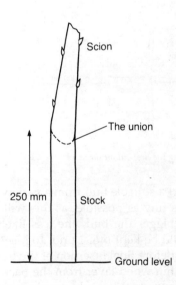

Whip and tongue grafting – stock and scion union

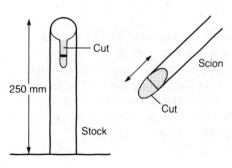

Whip and tongue grafting – stock and scion ready for joining

> **❗❗   REMEMBER**
>
> You must match the cambium tissue on stock and scion to create a union.

145

4. T-budding

Budding is a form of grafting and, like grafting, involves joining together a rootstock and a scion. It is long established and the accepted vegetative technique for the production of roses. There are two forms of rose production:

(i) T-shield budding
(ii) inverted T-shield budding.

T-shield budding is carried out low down on the rootstock, in fact at ground level. To keep the stock tender and in an acceptable condition for budding, once the stocks have been lined out in the field during winter they are earthed up. This will keep the hypocotyl region of the rootstock in a good condition for budding during the forthcoming summer.

T-shield budding – for example 'HT-Roses' (single flowered roses)

The budding technique

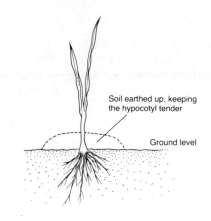

Earthing up rootstocks

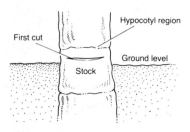

Identifying the hypocotyl region

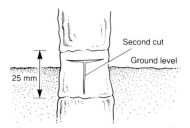

Decide where to cut on the hypocotyl

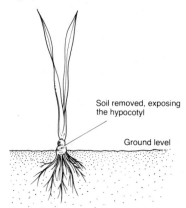

Hypocotyl exposure

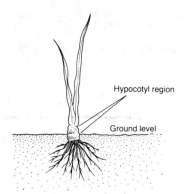

Making the first cut on the stock

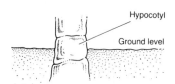

Making the second cut on the stock

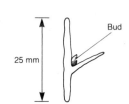

Preparing the bud

Select a suitable bud from a variety you wish to bud with. The bud should be as tiny as possible, as this will give a much better chance of a union. The bigger the bud, the less likely you are of achieving a union. Buds should be kept moist prior to insertion; it is vital you do not let them dry out. Before final insertion of the bud into the rootstock you should remove the thin wood layer from the back of the bud. This will mean once again that your bud has a better chance of making a union.

Bud insertion and tie

The cuts are pulled back and the bud is slotted in, the cut flaps being pushed back afterwards.

The tie is a simple rubber patch that will begin to degrade and then fall off after the bud has taken. T-shield budding is usually carried out in the summer, for example, July.

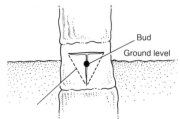

Flaps, produced as the second cut is peeled back, allowing the bud to be placed in

Bud insertion – after insertion, a rubber patch tie is placed over the bud to keep it in place

146

5. Chip Budding

This grafting technique is very similar to T-shield budding. The grafting principle is the same, using a bud, but chip budding is used for plant species other than roses. Once again, you are more likely to find it in the Commercial area of nursery stock production although the technique is used in Amenity Horticulture for small-scale propagation.

(a) The stock (rootstock)

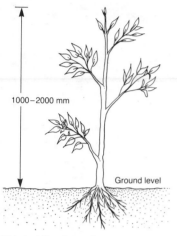

Chip budding the stock

Whips or 2-year-old liners are used. The height will depend on the species.

(b) Location of first cut on the stock

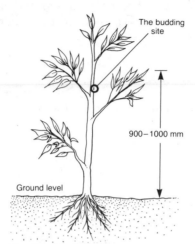

Identifying the budding site

Locate a suitable clean and clear site at approximately 900 mm from ground level, between two nodes.

(c) The first cut

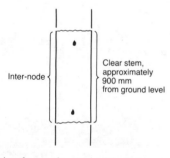

Selecting the actual position of the first cut

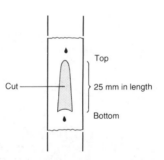

Preparing the stock

(i) Firstly, make a cut in the centre of the stem at the bottom end of the graft.

(ii) Secondly, measure approximately 25 mm up from that cut and then make a cut down to meet the first cut. This second cut is only to remove the skin layer.

(d) Preparing the bud

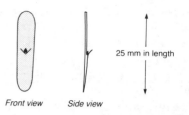

Preparing the bud

Firstly, remove the bud from the budstick, then remove the wood layer from behind the bud. Keep the bud moist prior to insertion.

(e) The graft union

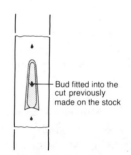

Joining the bud to the stock

The bud is inserted into the stock cut and then tied in using grafting polythene, tying in beneath and above the bud. Once the bud is deemed to have taken, the tie can be cut/released.

Chip budding is usually carried out during the summer.

▶▶▶ **TO DO**

Name four other grafting techniques, together with a suitable plant species for each.

---

6. Micro-Propagation

Micro-propagation is a laboratory technique used to propagate plants from small pieces of plant tissue. It is by no means a new technique, indeed scientists were working on the technique in the early 1900s. However, its real commercial potential was not seen until the early 1960s. Now the technique has become widely accepted in the Commercial world for the propagation of plants. It is not normally a viable proposition in Amenity Horticulture.

The technique of micro-propagation uses plant tissue which is grown on in cultures. It provides a quick vegetative propagation method that involves a number of clearly defined stages:

1. Preparation of stock plants: select the desired variety of plant and grow them on in a heated glasshouse. Water them using low level irrigation techniques. The resultant new growth should be good clean material.
2. Starting off the culture: remove the chosen pieces of tissue, for example, shoot tips or a section of leaf. The material is then sterilised and placed onto a nutrient agar gel medium.
3. Multiplication of tissue: after tissue establishment, the culture produces new shoots, and in turn these new shoots can be removed and cultured in the same manner as for the original culture.
4. Rooting: once you have a good number of shoots, they can be placed into a suitable growing-on medium in which they can begin to develop roots.
5. The weaning process: once sufficient roots have been produced, they can be placed into a suitable compost mix for growing on. They will need a specially designed growing-on environment where all the growing conditions are controlled, so that they can be weaned. After weaning, they should be ready to stand as new plants in their own right.

Propagation Environments

To aid successful seed germination or vegetative propagation, the right propagation environment is very important. No matter how well you have sown your seed or taken your cuttings, the germination environment for seed and the rooting environment for cuttings play an integral part of their propagation.

Propagation Environments for Seed

(a) *Examples of Indoor Environments*

(i) *Seed Tray and Propagator*

Many different types of seed can be successfully germinated in a simple seed tray and propagator top, as is shown in the picture. Seeds sown at the right time of year in such an environment and placed in a heated glasshouse generally respond very well. This basic propagation device can be made more sophisticated by introducing a soil-warming cable to provide bottom heat, which is vital for germination of some seeds. Remove the top after germination.

Seed tray and propagator

(ii) *Seed Tray, Glass and Paper*

This simple but popular environment is used for the propagation of many well known plants, for example, half-hardy annuals (bedding plants). The seed tray is placed on a bench after seed sowing and a sheet of glass is placed over it. Then the tray is covered with paper to block out the light. At the first sign of germination, remove the glass and paper.

This propagation environment can also be used on plant pots and is especially useful where small quantities of seed are to be sown.

Seed tray, glass and paper

(b) *Examples of Outdoor Environments*

(i) Drills in soil – seed sown in drills, for example wallflowers.
(ii) Broadcast – seed sown by broadcasting over the soil, for example, grass.
(iii) Cold frames – seed sown directly into cold frames, either in drills or by broadcast methods, or seed is sown in containers and then placed in cold frames, for example, alpines.

 TO DO

Some seeds actually need light for germination. Find out two examples.

Examples of Propagation Environments for Vegetative Propagation

(A) *Plant Pot and Polythene Bag*

This environment gives simple but effective aid to the propagation of cuttings. However, it is only used on a very small scale. The environment will maintain a high humidity (moisture in the air) which in turn will help reduce the transpiration rate of the cuttings (loss of water); loss of water is critical to the survival of cuttings, particularly those that are soft and fleshy, for example, *Pelargonium*. The polythene will also permit the passage of oxygen and carbon dioxide, which are both necessary for the growth processes of the cuttings.

(B) *Propagation Case*

Propagation cases can either be built indoors, for example, on a glasshouse bench, or outdoors in much the same way as a cold frame. They are often used indoors and are easily made from treated wood and assembled on the glasshouse bench. If they are placed inside a heated glasshouse, they may not require any supplementary heating. However, if they are sited in a cold glasshouse, soil-warming cables can be used. The top of the case can be made from either glass or polythene; provision should be made to enable shading to be applied to the tops of propagation cases in due course. A suitable white-wash material could be used on glass, while various other materials could be used on polythene.

Pot of cuttings and polythene bag

Indoor propagation case

 TIP

Beware of too much humidity in the environment. It is advisable at regular intervals to remove the polythene and shake off the excess moisture, and then replace it over the cuttings.

! !   REMEMBER

Cuttings in this environment are susceptible to diseases, particularly those that thrive in moist, humid conditions, for example, Grey Mould (Botrytis). To help prevent this, spray the cuttings with a systemic fungicide (such as benomyl) before insertion.

Advantages and Disadvantages of Propagation Cases

(i) Advantages
- cheap and easy to make
- they do not rely on any sophisticated machinery mechanisms
- if the right type of cutting taken at the right time of year is inserted into the propagation case, it can be an efficient environment for the rooting of cuttings
- cuttings can be direct stuck or inserted into seed trays or pots, which will provide you with mobility at a later date.

(ii) Disadvantages
- there can be a problem with poor air circulation
- compost can become too wet (this really depends on the compost used)
- direct stuck cuttings from propagation cases often have a problem with initial transplanting after rooting.

(C) *Cold Frames*

Cold frame

> ### ✱ FOR INTEREST
>
> Cold frames can be heated, using small-bore heating pipes connected to a suitable boiler. This will produce a mini-glasshouse environment.

Cold frames are still used today as a propagation environment for either seed or vegetative propagating techniques. Traditionally, they are built of brick and wood, and have used either Dutch Lights or English Lights for the top and cover of the frame. Alternatively, today frames can be made from less substantial materials such as plastic and polythene; these types of frame are easily erected and dismantled for moving purposes, and they are also much cheaper than traditional cold frames.

Dutch Light dimensions: 1.5 m × 750 mm.

English Light dimensions: 1.82 m × 1.37 m.

Cold frames as propagators: the following examples show the range of propagation techniques associated with a cold frame:

(a) tree and shrub seed sowing/germination;
(b) semi-ripe cuttings of shrubs and trees;
(c) hardwood cuttings of shrubs and trees;
(d) flower seed sowing/germination.

(D) *Cloches*

For small-scale propagation, cloches can be useful. They can provide a suitable environment for either outdoor seed germination or the rooting of cuttings which have been direct stuck in the nursery soil. Traditional cloches were made out of glass and clipped together with wire clips, today plastic and polythene are a cheaper alternative.

(E) *Low Polythene Tunnels*

Low polythene tunnels are constructed from polythene strips which are held tightly onto wire hoops with cross strings or wires. They are a low-cost propagation environment suitable for softwood, semi-ripe and hardwood cuttings. These tunnels can be easily and quickly erected outdoors or inside larger polythene houses or glasshouses. This latter method is widely used in the nursery stock industry and generally produces good results.

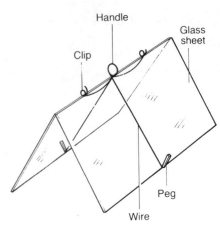

A traditional glass cloche

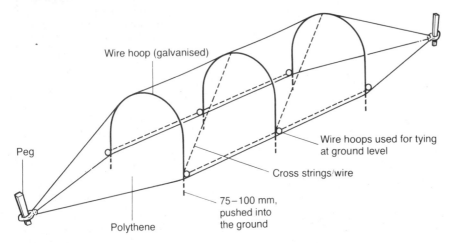

Low polythene tunnel assembly

(F) *Walk-in Polythene House*

Walk in polythene houses are widely used in both Amenity and Commercial Horticulture, mainly for growing-on purposes, but they can also be used to create a propagation environment. Semi-ripe cuttings of a whole range of shrubs can be direct stuck inside these tunnels, producing very good results at a later date.

(G) *Glasshouses*

Glasshouses are often used as an environment to aid the propagation of plants; such houses can be partially or fully heated as required. The environment afforded by glasshouses will often promote the germination of seed or the rooting of cuttings in its own right.

> **! ! REMEMBER**
>
> We have already seen where the glasshouse bench supports other propagation environments also.

Propagation house

Polythene house

Mist unit

The Working Parts of Mist Units

(a) Soil-warming cables – provide basal warming for the cuttings.

(b) Control thermostat – controls the heat output of the soil-warming cables, giving temperature control on the bench.

(c) Electronic leaf – this actually mimics a leaf surface and controls the frequency of misting. It consists of a piece of plastic in which are embedded two terminals which in turn are connected to the main control panel. When the terminals become wet, the electrical circuit is complete, operating the solenoid valve to cut off the water supply. When the electronic leaf is placed among the cuttings on the bench, its terminals dry off at a similar rate to the water drying off the surface of the plant's leaves. So, when the film of water connecting the terminals is broken again, the mist is switched on by the solenoid valve until finally the film of water is complete.

(d) Atomiser jets – these jets turn the water supply into a fine mist. The jets themselves are of the deflector type, which means that the mist is formed by allowing a thin jet of water to strike a flat surface. The atomiser jets are mounted on uprights (stand pipes), which in turn are connected to a water pipe that runs the length of the bench. For equal misting, the jets should be placed approximately 1000 mm apart on the bench.

(e) Pipework – a series of waterpipes and standpipes connected to a mains water supply is required.

(f) Solenoid valve – this valve regulates the flow of water; it is electrically operated via the main control panel.

(g) Filters – the Y-shaped filter is designed to sift out any water impurities within the water supply. It should be sited between the solenoid valve and the shut-off valve of the mains water supply.

Mist Units and Propagation

An intermittent mist unit has already been described; it is so called because it comes on and goes off as appropriate. In both Amenity and Commercial Horticulture it is widely used to propagate a very wide range of plants. For most plants that can be propagated it is a near perfect rooting environment. As a propagation aid it is sophisticated but expensive both to install and to maintain compared with the other environments we have looked at. However, its main advantage is in rooting plants very quickly, including species that were once thought very hard or even difficult to root by vegetative means.

It is most useful for the speedy rooting of:

1. houseplants
2. shrubs
3. conifers
4. (some) evergreens and deciduous trees.

Softwood stem cuttings of houseplants and shrubs are invariably easy and quick to root once they are put under mist.

Advantages of Mist for the Rooting of Cuttings

1. Mist will reduce transpiration and respiration of cuttings.
2. It will increase the survival of cuttings, particularly of softwoods.
3. It increases the relative humidity.
4. It allows the full use of light; this is important to the cutting as it allows maximum photosynthesis.
5. It generally produces roots more quickly.

Disadvantages of Mist

1. It is dependent on machinery.
2. A power failure will close it down.
3. Not all plant species are suitable for mist. Those characterised by having hairs on their leaves will not do well if placed under mist.
4. It is an expensive method of propagating plants.

Weaner units: once cuttings are rooted (in trays/pots), they can be transferred to the weaner unit. The misting in this unit is less frequent than the parent unit, allowing the cuttings to harden-off much as they do in a glasshouse and cold frame.

✱ FOR INTEREST

Weaner units give newly rooted 'mist' cuttings the opportunity to harden-off from the parent mist bench, providing similar conditions but much less frequently.

Growing on Young Plants

Houseplants

Once your plants are rooted, you must decide how you will grow them on. For houseplants and pot plants this is easy and straightforward. Houseplants and pot plants will need protection (many require constant heating) so they are best grown on inside a heated protective structure, like a glasshouse. The houseplants and pot plants we have already considered in chapter 6 are all grown on in heated glasshouses. How much these plants are grown on depends on the plant you are trying to produce. For example, if you want to produce large foliage plants suitable for decorative work, then they will need a reasonable time to grow and develop. For houseplants or pot plants, all the young plants will be containerised – so you only need to decide on the size and type of container you will use.

How much heat is required for the growing on will depend on the individual plant species. You need to know what temperature plants or crops require for successful growth and development.

Houseplants in containers

▶ ▶ ▶   **TO DO**

Suggest the appropriate growing on temperatures for the following houseplants:

1. Rubber plant (*Ficus*)
2. Bird of Paradise Flower (*Strelitzia*)
3. Poinsettia (*Euphorbia*)
4. Joseph's Coat (*Codaeium*)
5. Wandering Jew (*Tradescantia*)
6. Bottle Brush Plant (*Callistemon*).

How many of these plants did you know?

! !   **REMEMBER**

If your plants are specifically grown for decorative work, flowering pot plants are only seasonal and short term. However, foliage plants are long lasting, therefore growing-on space is an important consideration for these plants. They will need a good deal of your glasshouse bench space.

Nursery Stock

Nursery Stock can be propagated either by seed or by various vegetative techniques.

Seedlings that have grown from seed under protective structures are often pricked off into various sizes and types of container. However, when the seed is direct sown in cold frames, it can be containerised or lined out in suitably prepared nursery beds.

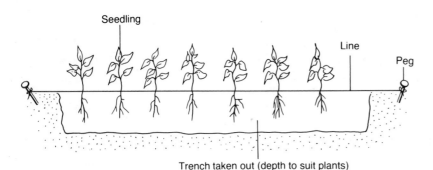

Lining out

In its development, the seedling is beginning the next phase of its life, leaving behind the propagative phase and moving into the growing-on phase.

Cuttings propagated by vegetative techniques need to be grown on in much the same way as for seedlings. Rooted cuttings have the same two alternatives available to them as have seedlings. You will need to decide whether your rooted cuttings should be containerised or lined out in the nursery.

If you choose to line out the young plants in the field, then obviously they will be exposed to all the different climatic conditions experienced throughout the year. Try to make sure your plants are hardy if you choose this method of growing on.

If you choose to containerise your plants, they can be grown on using various protective structures.

✳ FOR INTEREST

Nursery stock that is grown on by being lined out in prepared nursery beds is often known as 'field-grown' stock. In due course, this stock can be lifted and either planted as bare rooted plants or containerised or root-balled.

✳ FOR INTEREST

Nursery stock refers to the production of young plants. Hardy nursery stock refers to the production of those plants that are considered hardy, for example, the majority of trees and shrubs.

Growing On Nursery Stock in Protective Structures

Young plants that are containerised after rooting are often grown on using one or a combination of the following:

1. Polythene houses –
   (a) Conventional houses with rounded sides
   (b) Houses with straight sides
   (c) Woven plastic covered houses

2. Outdoor capillary beds

3. Sand beds

4. Outdoor standing ground –
   (a) Soil surface covered with black polythene which in turn is covered with a lime-free sand layer
   (b) Soil surface covered with black polythene which in turn is covered with chippings.

1. Polythene Houses

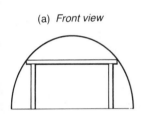
(a) *Front view*

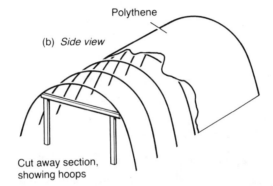
Polythene

(b) *Side view*

Cut away section, showing hoops

Polythene houses

(a) Conventional houses

Walk-in polythene houses are of great use for the growing on of containerised young plants; they give the plants a good deal of protection, not least from wind.

Young plants tend to do well in these houses but take care that they do not stay too long in this growing-on environment, as they may produce too much fleshy growth which can be susceptible to cooler outside conditions.

Polythene houses are also useful in promoting the early growth of stock plants. Stock plants of various species can be brought into these houses in mid winter; in this way any early growth they produce could be used as cutting material, therefore giving you a head start in propagation. Examples of plants where this technique could be used include *Azalea*, Magnolias, Hebes, *Spiraea*, and some of the Japanese Acers. No artificial heat requirement is needed for this – we simply rely on the winter sun to warm up the houses.

TIP

Learn to call them walk-in polythene houses. This then should stop any misunderstanding there might be between these houses and low tunnels.

! ! REMEMBER

Wind can easily dry out containers. Any protection you can give plants, particularly while they are young, is of great value to the plant.

(b) Houses with straight sides

These are conventional walk-in polythene houses with straight sides of approximately 1 m height, made from a woven plastic or other windbreak material. The advantage of having a straight-sided house is that, in practice, more plants should be able to stand in these houses since no area is lost at their edges as is the case with conventional houses. Also, because the material used for the sides is porous, it adds to the ventilation of the house and allows the plants a more outdoor type of climate, yet still giving good protection.

(c) Woven-plastic-covered houses

These are built from a woven plastic material (porous) which can be bought in various thicknesses/grades. Woven plastic is essentially a windbreak material but, according to the grade you choose, it can also offer varying degrees of shade. For many hardy plants, some shading is beneficial during growing on. For example, partial shade would be very appropriate for the following young hardy nursery stock:

1. *Pieris* species
2. *Azalea* species
3. *Rhododendron* species
4. Various evergreen species, for example 'evergreen' *Viburnum*.

2. Outdoor Capillary Beds

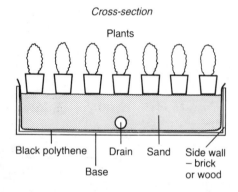

Cross-section

Plants

Black polythene | Drain | Sand | Side wall
– brick
or wood

Base

Outdoor capillary beds

Although capillary beds can be used both indoors and outdoors, they are most often used outdoors in conjunction with hardy nursery stock. Such beds maintain a moisture level (fairly constant) by automatic means.

3. Sand Beds (inside or outside use)

These are growing-on beds made of sand and, unlike capillary beds, they do not have to be automatically watered. Sand beds can simply be irrigated in the normal way as and when necessary to maintain the moisture levels of the sand. They are a cheap yet effective alternative to capillary beds.

 TO DO

Find out just how a capillary bed works. Does your college horticulture department have any? Perhaps a local nurseryman can help.

4. Outdoor Standing Ground

(a) Black polythene and lime-free sand: a suitable area of land is found, which must be level and free from debris. Black polythene of an appropriate thickness is spread over the surface and this is then covered with sand, a thin layer (25 mm) being adequate. Containerised nursery stock is then lined out on this area for growing on.

Black polythene and sand

(b) Black polythene and chippings: treat as in (a).

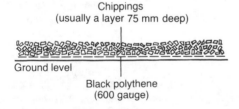

Chippings
(usually a layer 75 mm deep)

Ground level

Black polythene
(600 gauge)

Black polythene and chippings make a useful weed-free standing area

Practical Protection

All growing-on areas, polythene houses and outdoor field beds need to be protected from wind. The damage caused to young plants by wind can be devastating, as it often comes at a time when the plants have no real resistance.

Windbreaks should be considered as an integral and very important part of a nursery. However, their effectiveness depends on numerous factors, not least of which is the type of material they are made from. Traditionally, hedges (various species used) have been used for windbreaks but today a variety of synthetic/artificial substitutes is used.

✳ FOR INTEREST

Capillary beds, sand beds and outdoor beds may from time to time be attacked by disease organisms, lichen, mosses and other weeds. You should apply the appropriate pesticide control measures as early as is practically possible.

 TO DO

Make a list of six different plants that can be used as hedges/windbreaks for a nursery.
Also make a short list of some of the artificial materials that are used. How many do you know?

 TO DO

Make a list of the advantages you consider windbreaks bring to the nursery.
Can you think of any disadvantages of windbreaks?

INDEX